ABOUT THE AUTHORS

DR MARTIN COLE began his professional career as a biologist and until 1984 lectured in genetics and social and reproductive biology at the University of Aston. However he is most well known for his work in sex education and sex therapy and currently practises sex therapy privately.

He was co-founder of the Birmingham Brook Advisory Centre, founder of the Birmingham Pregnancy Advisory Service which later became the British Pregnancy Advisory Service, and founder of the Institute for Sex Education and Research. He has made several films on sex education and therapy, and written numerous articles for newspapers and magazines. This is his second book.

DR WINDY DRYDEN is Senior Lecturer in psychology at Goldsmith's College, University of London and practises part-time as a psychotherapist at St. Thomas's Hospital, London and at the Raphael Counselling Centre, London.

He is a Fellow of the British Psychological Society and serves on the editorial boards of several professional journals on psychotherapy and counselling. This is his fourth book.

SEX PROBLEMS

YOUR QUESTIONS ANSWERED

MARTIN COLE
AND
WINDY DRYDEN

ILLUSTRATED BY JOANNA CAMERON

An OPTIMA book

© Martin Cole and Windy Dryden 1989

First published in 1989 by
Macdonald Optima, a division of
Macdonald & Co. (Publishers) Ltd

A member of Maxwell Pergamon Publishing Corporation plc

British Library Cataloguing in Publication Data

Cole, Martin, *1931–*
  Sex problems
  1. Man. Sexual disorders. Therapy
  I. Title II. Dryden, Windy
  616.6′906

  ISBN 0-356-15985-X

Macdonald & Co. (Publishers) Ltd
66–73 Shoe Lane
London EC4P 4AB

Printed and bound in Great Britain by
The Guernsey Press Co. Ltd
Guernsey
Channel Islands

CONTENTS

To Lisa

Acknowledgment

We wish to thank Consella Parkinson
for her help in preparing the manuscript
for this book: her graduation from the
typewriter to the word processor had
to be seen to be believed!

INTRODUCTION

It is a common experience of sex therapists that they find it very difficult, if not impossible, to be able to select one comprehensive book on sexual problems that they can recommend to all their clients or patients, knowing that it will provide most of the information they require in a popular and readable style. Many books on this subject are either directed at a specialized professional readership – and are therefore too heavy-going for the average reader – or they cover only part of the subject. Some are also very expensive.

This book hopes to fill this gap. It is written in an easily understandable style and, in particular, it is presented in a way that will enable the reader to find quickly the information he or she wants. The question-and-answer format, which is a feature of the book and one not used in others on the same subject, will provide the reader with a ready access to most aspects of sexual problems and sex therapy.

At least one person in ten of reproductive age has a disabling sexual problem that is sufficient to make intercourse either very difficult or certainly not very rewarding. In addition, of many marriages that are likely to end in divorce, the break-up of a signficiant majority of them will have been caused by sexual difficulties. It is for these people that this book is written.

1.
QUESTIONS AND ANSWERS ABOUT SEX

The main purpose of this book is to provide some of the answers to the many questions that people ask about sexual difficulties they may encounter. However, there are, of course, many other questions in peoples' minds that are not necessarily related to sexual problems: therefore in this short introductory chapter we have provided answers to some of these more general questions that are often asked.

Is masturbation good for you?
This question is like asking 'Is climbing a mountain good for you?' – it all depends on whether you enjoy climbing mountains. Masturbation is certainly never bad for you, and indeed, it is probably impossible to masturbate too much because, after a time, you would simply stop because it was no longer enjoyable.

For many men and women who have no regular sexual partners, self-masturbation may provide them with their only source of sexual pleasure; as such, it is very important for them, particularly if they are able to enjoy exciting sexual fantasies while they masturbate. It is also important for men who do not have a regular opportunity for intercourse to continue to masturbate to orgasm if only to keep the physiological and psychological mechanisms ticking over: too long a period of abstinence may lead to problems with erection when the man does eventually

1

find a sexual partner. However, it should be recognized that some men (and many more women) do not enjoy masturbating; they would rather go without an orgasm and wait until they find a partner.

Masturbation looms large during adolescence. Before teenagers reach the psychological age of readiness for intercourse, there may be a period of several years when masturbation and fantasy provide the only means of obtaining release from sexual frustration. Therefore, at this time of life, masturbation is obviously particularly important, especially for the adolescent boy: in him, masturbation and the accompanying fantasies act as a kind of rehearsal for intercourse.

How much semen does a man produce when he ejaculates?

During most of his adult life, with ejaculation taking place, say, two or three times a week, a man will usually produce an ejaculate of about 4 millilitres – a largish teaspoonful. A young man will normally produce more and an older man less, and of course, the more frequently a man ejaculates, the volume of semen produced will be reduced proportionately. In addition, some men consistently produce more semen than others; there is a normal range in volume from about 1 to 6 millilitres.

Does smoking affect a man's sex drive and capacity to become aroused?

There is some evidence that, although not yet fully substantiated, does suggest that smoking cigarettes may affect some men's capacity to achieve a good erection. Some men report that smoking just two or three cigarettes a day affects them sexually, but obviously, not every man is likely to be affected in this way.

Will stimulating a woman's nipple during intercourse help her to have an orgasm?

This depends very much on the individual. Some women have very sensitive nipples and others do not. A woman will usually discover this for herself and may massage her own nipples when she masturbates or will ask her partner to suck them when they are making love.

One of the reasons why nipple stimulation may arouse a woman and help her to climax is that, when women breastfeed, the stimulation of the baby sucking the nipple raises levels of the hormone *oxytocin*. This usually functions to stimulate the secretions of the breastmilk, but oxytocin also has the effect of stimulating the contraction of the muscles of the uterus and therefore may help some women to achieve orgasm.

Why do we have pubic hair?

Perhaps the most important reason why pubic hair develops at puberty is to tell other people that this person has either reached or is rapidly approaching sexual maturity. The growth of hair is a very effective way of communicating signals to other members of a social group. For example, the growth of a beard in a man will signal his sexual maturity, and the appearance of grey hair normally signals advancing years.

Pubic hair also performs the important function of protecting the pubic area from the bruising and soreness that might occur following frequent and prolonged intercourse. Finally, pubic hair serves to trap body odours and the special substances known as *pheromones*, which may play an important part in the process of sexual attraction and arousal.

What is the average length of a man's penis when it is erect and unerect?

When the penis is soft and flaccid, as it is in an

unaroused man, its average length is just under 4 inches when measured along the top, from the pubic hair to the tip, or *glans penis*. When it is stiff and erect, its average length increases to just over 6 inches. There is, however, a considerable variation in penis size from one man to another. Unerect, it can be as short as 2 inches or as long as 6 inches or more, and when erect, the size can vary from under 4 inches to over 8 inches. The longest erect penis recorded by Alfred Kinsey, the author of the famous *Kinsey Report*[1], was over 9¼ inches, though the authors are sure that this record could easily be beaten.

Because men are so self-conscious about the sizes of their penises, it is worth stressing that there is much more variation in the length of the penis when it is flaccid than when it is erect. In other words, men with relatively small unerect penises often catch up with their better-endowed friends when they get an erection because the smaller organ increases in length proportionately more than the longer unerect organ. Since men normally make comparisons between each other when they are in the showers or changing room and rarely see each other's penises when they are erect, they may get quite the wrong impression about the size of their friend's penises and worry unnecessarily.

If a man thinks his penis is too small, how can he be reassured?

Men who consider their penises to be too small – and women who are concerned about the size and shape of their breasts – often worry because they feel sexually underconfident and unsure about themselves, and seize upon what they believe to be any tangible signs of inadequacy to justify their anxieties; they may, in extreme cases, even use this as an excuse for not entering into relationships.

Since the average length of an erect penis is 6 inches, half of all men will have a penis 6 inches or less in length. This variation is normal, and since absolutely nothing can be done to increase the length of the penis (despite claims to the contrary), it is important to be able to accept the way you are. Men should also remember that most women claim that the size of a penis is not important and does not affect a man's ability to arouse them and bring them to orgasm.

Is anal intercourse harmful?

The anus is a ring of muscular tissue at the opening of the rectum in which solid waste is held. Although the entrance to the rectum is normally closed, it is rarely difficult in an adult to insert the little finger into the anus, particularly if some lubricant is used; some couples do this to each other regularly when they make love. Alternatively, they may insert a vibrator into the rectum to provide added stimulation. There is no harm in this, though great care should be taken not to push the vibrator (or any other object) in too far – surgeons, more frequently than would commonly be imagined, have to operate in order to remove lost items from within the rectum!

Full anal intercourse is not uncommon between men and women – as many as one in five report that they have enjoyed this kind of sex play. Perhaps the only problem is the risk of infection, but on balance, this is probably not much greater than that arising from vaginal intercourse, with the notable exception of AIDS.

Can a man remain sexually active with one testicle?

Yes: it makes no difference except that the other testis grows much larger to compensate for the loss. Even if a man loses both his testicles, the hormone *testosterone*, which is normally produced by the testes, can be easily replaced by tablets or injections. The loss of both testes will, of course, result in the man becoming sterile.

Is it safe for a woman to have intercourse when she is pregnant?

Unless there is a history of miscarriage or a risk of a sexually transmitted infection, intercourse is perfectly safe throughout pregnancy.

Some women say that they feel more sexy when they are pregnant. However, usually after the second month, there is a steady decline in their sex drive as the pregnancy progresses. Therefore, the best judge of whether to make love or not is the woman herself. Some men, of course, find that they are not sexually aroused by their partners when they are pregnant (although others feel exactly the opposite), and this fact may contribute to the incidence of reports that intercourse is less popular during pregnancy.

After childbirth, a woman's tissues must be given time to heal (up to six weeks) before full intercourse should be attempted, and there is also usually a period lasting perhaps several months when the frequency of intercourse remains low. A lot of adjustments have to be made by both the mother and the father of the newborn child, and it is important that the woman in particular is given time to readjust both physiologically and psychologically to sex after the birth of her child.

What are multiple orgasms?

Normally, when a man has an orgasm and ejaculates, he needs to wait a while before he can climax again. For a man in his teens and early 20s, this interval may be very short – perhaps only a few minutes – but as he gets older, this so-called *refractory period* gets longer until, in his 40s or 50s, he may only be able to obtain one orgasm a day. There is naturally a considerable variation in this response between different men.

A woman, on the other hand, is made differently. She can have orgasms one after the other and this is what is known as multiple orgasm. Some women, though by no means all, are capable of two, three or even four climaxes every time they make love, and there is even a rare response called *status orgasmus* in which the woman experiences one long, continuous orgasm lasting for several minutes. Kinsey reported that about one woman in ten experiences multiple orgasms during intercourse.

Is it normal for young boys to get erections?

Erection of the penis can, and does, occur throughout life from birth to death. It is often observed in young babies (and even in the unborn child in the uterus) and will continue throughout childhood. Most of these erections will take place quite spontaneously (for example, in the bath) and do not mean that the boy is feeling sexually aroused. Of course, he may obtain some pleasure and comfort from stimulating his penis (as does a girl touching her vulva), and parents must get used to the idea that this is perfectly natural and not react to his erection one way or the other, however embarrassed they may feel.

Why do people get jealous?

It is a fact of life that men become jealous of their woman and women of their men. This is because the need to bond and form relationships is a powerful biological drive, and if for any reason this bond is threatened, the hurt and rejected partner will respond to try and protect the relationship. The mixture of feelings that we call jealousy – loss, grief, anger, fear – is quite normal; it is nature's way of saying that there is something wrong with a relationship.

As a result of these emotions and the arguments that take place, the couple may begin to communicate more honestly with each other, with the result that the relationship either stabilizes or founders. To the extent that they engender communication, jealous feelings are good. Sometimes, however, jealousy is based not on a real threat to the relationship but on an imaginary one. In such a case, help from outside may become necessary if the relationship is to be saved, since these irrational feelings can be very destructive. However, even if a relationship does end, most people survive the loss of a partner and come to terms with it, the passage of time being a great healer. Some people are particularly possessive and jealous of their partners: this is usually because they are insecure in all their relationships, they do not value themselves sufficiently and feel basically unlovable.

Why are men generally more jealous than women?
Although the differences between the sexes are slowly disappearing, it is still true to say that, on average, men are more jealous than women. This difference is part of the old double standard which, in turn, has its roots in the biological differences between the sexes. A woman will always know that she is the biological mother of her child, but a father can *never* know for sure (without subsequent tests). However, as long as he is responsible for the welfare and survival of his partner and his children, it is clearly in his interest to be as sure as he can that these *are* his children; otherwise he will be providing resources (income, shelter and support) for children that may not be his own, and it does not make biological sense to favour the survival of another man's genes. If, on the other hand, a man goes off and gets another woman pregnant, this does not (in biological terms) matter to his partner, as long as he comes back.

Why is it that, in some men, the penis is bent or curved when it becomes erect?
The penis becomes erect as a result of blood flowing into two rods of spongy tissue on either side of the penis. Sometimes one of these tissue rods expands more than the other, and this results in a slight curvature, to the left or right, of the erect penis. This is of no consequence and will not interfere with intercourse. There is also a condition known as *Peyronies disease*, recognized by the presence of hard and often painful

areas of tissue in the shaft of the penis, which will also produce some curvature of the penis when it is erect. When the penis curves downwards as a result of this disease (and other conditions), this is known as *chordee*.

Does being overweight affect your sex life?

Normal variation in body weight does not have very much effect upon a person's sex life. However, those who are medically defined as obese may find that they are less interested in sex. This may be because they feel less fit and are therefore less active; it may be because the excess fat has affected the production of sex hormones; or it may be that by over-eating and making themselves unattractive they have an excuse for not having a sexual relationship.

Those who are underweight may also lose interest in sex, sometimes much more dramatically. For example, women who suffer from anorexia nervosa (the so-called 'slimmer's disease') lose their sex drive completely and normally stop menstruating. A man who diets and falls well below his natural bodyweight will also lose interest in sex.

Can a man go on having erections and orgasms all his life?

Generally speaking, men between the ages of 50 and 60 will begin to notice that their interest in and need for sex is slowly beginning to decline. Those older men find that their capacity to ejaculate appears to lessen, and the speed with which the older man can get an erection will be much less than when he was younger.

However, there is so much variation between individual men in this respect that what is true for the 'average' man can be a little misleading. The extent to which a man retains his sexual performance will depend a lot on whether he has a partner to whom he is sexually attracted and who is also interested in making love with him. Some women lose interest in sex after the menopause (see below), and naturally this will affect her partner, who, feeling rejected, may simply decide that their sex lives are at an end. If some men in middle life go without sex for a year or so – say, after bereavement – they may find it difficult to start again and will need a very sympathetic partner. However, in the normal course of events, and assuming they are reasonably healthy, they are not taking any medication that is likely to affect their sexual performance and they have a willing partner, many men are capable of achieving an erection and ejaculating well into their seventh decade.

Is intercourse after menopause ever painful?
Menopause is the time in a woman's life when, at about 50, her ovaries stop producing ova (eggs) and she stops having periods. This is the end of her reproductive life, but in most cases, it is certainly not the end of her sex life.

After menopause, the ovaries stop functioning because the ova are no longer needed, but the ovaries are also responsible for the production of the two female hormones *oestrogen* and *progesterone*. At menopause, the secretion of these two hormones will also stop. A woman will not miss progesterone, which is the 'pregnancy hormone', but some do suffer from the effects of the loss of oestrogen. Oestrogen, among other things, is responsible for maintaining the readiness of the vulva and vagina for intercourse and, in particular, helps to lubricate these when she is aroused. One of the effects of oestrogen loss, therefore, is that the vulva and vagina may remain dry during intercourse, and this often produces some discomfort and pain.

Some oestrogens may be produced elsewhere in a woman's body, particularly in the fat of plumper women, but for those who find that intercourse has become painful, it is advisable to consult a doctor. Sometimes simply applying a little cream or KY jelly to the vagina will be all that is necessary;

alternatively, a cream containing oestrogen, also applied to the vagina, may work. Finally, the woman can be given *hormone replacement therapy* (HRT), when oestrogen is given in the form of tablets, an implant or injection.

Does male sterilization (vasectomy) or female sterilization affect a person's sex life?

The benefits of either male or female sterilization are obvious: if one or other is sterilized the couple know that the fear of an unwanted pregnancy has at last been removed and that love-making can be enjoyed without having to worry about using contraceptives. However, the sterilization operation is not easily reversed so the decision to go ahead must only be taken after very careful thought.

There is no evidence that either vasectomy or female sterilization adversely affects the quality of a person's sex life. Sometimes a man will have a vasectomy in the hope that it may help him with an existing problem such as premature ejaculation, and when it does not work, he may unjustly blame the worsening of his condition on the operation. Sometimes it is just a coincidence that the operation and some other event has triggered a sexual problem, and the operation once again gets the blame. Some women do report that they feel somewhat 'different' sexually after a sterilization operation, and occasionally say that they do not enjoy sex as much as before. However, there is no known medical reason why this should be so, and if the feelings persist, it is very likely that they are entirely psychological in origin.

It is well known that too much alcohol will affect the sexual performance of some men, but does drink also affect a woman's capacity to enjoy sex and have orgasms?

Just as some men drink ten pints of beer and still get a good erection, ejaculate and enjoy intercourse, so the

11

capacity of some women to enjoy sex when they have had a lot to drink also remains unchanged. However, generally speaking, women respond to alcohol in the same way as men – the more they drink, the less they are able to enjoy the physical experience of either intercourse or masturbation, even though they may feel less inhibited. Women often report, for example, that they feel numb and find it difficult to get really aroused.

Why is it that a couple who have a close and intimate relationship often find it difficult to share honest feelings about their sex lives?
Feelings such as shyness, modesty and guilt about sex are present in most of us, though obviously these feelings are more strongly expressed in some. Embarrassment about sex appears at quite an early age in children, and develops much more strongly in adolescence when, for example, many teenagers find it particularly difficult to communicate with their parents about sex in relationships. (The same can be true for parents, who often find it equally difficult to communicate with their children – incidentally, one of the best arguments in favour of schools taking responsibility for sex education.)

These same feelings of embarrassment and shyness about sex also frequently prevent a husband and wife, or boyfriend and girlfriend, from talking easily and naturally to one another about sex. Probably these communication problems are part of the incest taboo, an inborn dislike of mixing sex and intimacy. Making love is one thing, but talking about it often appears to be more difficult. Men seem to be victims of this kind of embarrassment much more frequently than women: if, as part of therapy, it is necessary for a couple to start talking openly and honestly to each other, it may be easier for her rather than him to break the ice.

What are 'poppers'? Are they aphrodisiacs?

'Poppers' are capsules or vials of ethyl nitrite. Its immediate effect, if it is inhaled, is to dilate the blood vessels throughout the body, which in turn produces a sudden drop in blood pressure. The body then responds to this by secreting the hormone *adrenalin* to constrict the blood vessels and restore the blood pressure to normal.

Some men and women sniff this substance during love-making because they believe it gives them a better orgasm. The idea is to take a sniff a few minutes before a climax; it is thought that the rise in blood pressure, brought on by the body's secretion of adrenalin, improves the quality of the orgasm. Using 'poppers' is probably not dangerous – for example, they are not addictive – but their use can produce side-effects such as severe headaches. In addition, nobody with a hint of a heart or circulatory disorder should experiment with 'poppers'.

Is it safe to swallow a man's semen when he ejaculates into your mouth during oral sex?

Yes: as long as the man is free from any infection, semen is quite harmless. Claims made for its nutritional qualities may be somewhat over-exaggerated, but even more than most variations in sexual practice, this particular indulgence is simply a matter of taste.

Is it all right for a woman to have sex when she is having a period?

A lot of men do not like making love to a woman when she is menstruating, and many women do not like it either. Probably around half of all lovers do not have intercourse during the time when the woman is having a period for purely personal reasons. In addition, there are some religions – Judaism and Islam, for example – where intercourse is taboo at this time. However, a lot of menstruating women do feel particularly sexy, and of course, it is also very unlikely (though not impossible) to conceive during menstruation, so there are certain advantages to be gained from making love at this time.

Is it normal for a woman to bleed from her vagina after intercourse?

A woman may bleed a little when she loses her virginity. Kinsey reported that well over half of young American girls in the 1950s bled at least a little when they made love for the first time. However, with the wider use of internal tampons, a more liberated view of female masturbation and more adventurous sex play between the sexes before intercourse takes place, the vagina is often already sufficiently stretched that bleeding at first intercourse is much rarer nowadays.

However, once a woman has begun to have regular intercourse, she should not bleed after making love. If a man notices blood on his penis after intercourse, on an occasion other than when his partner is having a period, this may indicate that something is wrong, and the woman should seek medical advice to establish the cause of her bleeding.

Why do some women cry when they or their partners have an orgasm during intercourse?

Crying is a way of expressing deeply felt feelings such as anger, pain, sadness or joy, particularly if these emotions come upon you suddenly. Crying after intercourse may, therefore, result from the sudden release of physical and emotional tension after an orgasm. However, tears are more likely to be a woman's way of expressing more subtle and complicated feelings whether it is her orgasm or his that triggers this response.

Although we are encouraged to believe that men do not cry, it would be surprising if there were not a few men who, if they were honest, would also admit that they have also cried after a particularly significant experience of intercourse.

2.
DIFFICULTIES WITH ERECTION

Men who cannot get rigid enough erections to penetrate the vagina, or are unable to remain hard enough to enjoy intercourse are often deeply distressed. However, much can be done nowadays to help those who have difficulties of this kind and advice should be sought as soon as possible.

What kinds of difficulties is a man likely to experience with his erection?
In order for intercourse to take place satisfactorily, the normally soft penis needs to become much larger and more rigid in order to penetrate the vagina. To achieve this, blood flows into the penis, which then lengthens and thickens. As it becomes erect, it also becomes much harder and sticks out in front of the man's body at an angle that may vary from near horizontal to almost vertical – a variation that, incidentally, is quite normal.

It is not uncommon for a man to have problems with his erection. Anything from being over-tired to having too much to drink may lead to a temporary loss of the ability to achieve an erection. However, the difficulties may be more serious. If they have always been present and, as a result, intercourse has never been achieved, they are known as *primary* erectile problems; if, after having enjoyed a period of normal sex, a man later has difficulties in getting an erection, these are called *secondary* erectile problems.

Originally the word *impotence* was used by the medical profession to describe not only erectile problems but also those involving ejaculating either too quickly or too slowly (see pp. 46–69). We have decided not to use this word because of its imprecision; besides, like the word 'frigid', being labelled 'impotent' is not at all helpful and, moreover, can be disparaging.

How does erection occur?

One of the first things that happens to a man when he becomes sexually aroused is that he begins to get an erection. From whatever source the signals come – watching television, fantasy, physical contact in masturbation or from sex play with his partner – the brain processes this information and relays it through the nervous system to the penis. At the same time, changes will take place in the blood levels of the sex hormones that also play a part in the process of arousal.

Although the mechanism of erection is not fully understood, it is clear that the first response is for arteries in the penis to expand. These arteries deliver blood to the erectile tissues, made up of three rods of elastic, spongy tissue honeycombed with spaces that fill with blood on erection. As the arteries dilate and the erectile tissues expand, the veins that normally drain blood away become compressed, slowing down the loss of blood from the penis. Since the inflow of blood is greater than the outflow, the penis will, in normal circumstances, then become hard and erect. After ejaculation (or some time later if ejaculation is not appropriate), the arteries contract, the erectile rods shrink and soften and the veins open to drain the blood away. The penis then returns to its original shape and size.

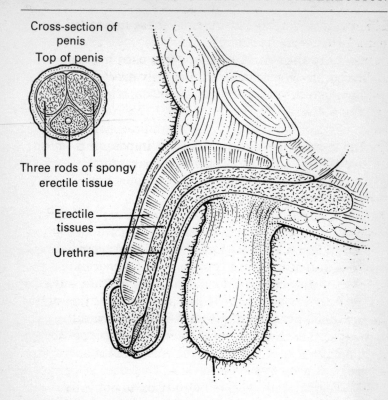

Cross-section of penis

Top of penis

Three rods of spongy erectile tissue

Erectile tissues

Urethra

Erectile tissues of the penis

How common are problems with erection?

Most men will be able to recall the odd occasion when they were unable to obtain an erection, but very often these were only temporary problems that sorted themselves out sooner or later. Reliable information about the frequency of more serious difficulties with erection is difficult to come by because, quite obviously, the frequency of the condition will vary according to the age of the people questioned. The noted American sexologist Alfred Kinsey, for example, found that, in 20-year-olds, only one in 1000 reported difficulties with erection, but when he studied 65-year-olds, this rate increased to 25 per cent. A more recent study published in 1987[2], in which a large number of men with the average age of 37 were questioned, showed that about

7 per cent had difficulties achieving an erection, and this figure is supported by other surveys[3]. There is no doubt that difficulties with erection are the most common problem brought to sex therapy clinics, and it is obviously a very worrying event for a lot of men of all ages.

What usually has gone wrong when a man has difficulty getting an erection?

At one time, it was thought that problems with erection were caused largely by anxiety, worry or a poor relationship. 'Go away and stop worrying, and all will be well' was the kind of advice GPs would normally give their distressed male patients who were having difficulties with erection. While there is no doubt that psychological causes are important in many cases, there is now a great deal of evidence that as many as 50 per cent of all erectile difficulties are probably caused by physical (medical) problems.

This division of the causes of erectile failure into those that are physical and those that are psychological, however, is not quite as simple as it sounds. This is because some of the physical problems that may reduce a man's capacity to get a really good erection would not by themselves prevent him from achieving intercourse; however, the fact that he now worries about his performance could then lead him to fail totally. In other words, physical and psychological causes can interact in a complicated way.

What can go wrong physically?

For a man to achieve a good erection, at least three physiological processes must be working adequately:
1. The circulation of the blood – that is, the arteries and veins serving the penis – must function properly.
2. The nerves that control the erectile process must be intact.
3. Hormone levels, particularly those concerned with sexual responses, must be within their normal ranges.

There are almost certainly other important factors, but very little is known about these at present.

If anything goes wrong with one or more of these physiological processes, a man's ability to achieve an erection can be affected to a greater or lesser extent.

What kinds of things can go wrong with the blood supply to the penis?

The rapid flow of sufficient blood into the erectile tissues of the penis is essential if a man is to get and maintain a good, rigid erection. Two types of problems may interfere with this process.

First, any disease of the arteries will reduce the speed and volume of blood flow by narrowing the diameter of the blood vessels. Usually this process is a very gradual one and will only affect middle-aged and older men. However, very occasionally, arterial disease also affects those who are younger. Occasionally, this can be cured surgically, but the man will also have to maintain a healthy lifestyle: no smoking; eating nutritiously and avoiding foods high in animal fat; taking enough exercise; and so on.

Second, the layout of the blood vessels in the penis may lead to what is known as a *venous leak*. This occurs when blood entering the base of the penis does not pass into the erectile tissue as it should but, instead, does a kind of 'U turn' and leaks across into the veins without playing its part in the erection process. This leakage prevents a full erection from ever forming, in the same way as puncture may prevent a tyre from inflating however hard the latter is pumped up. This malformation of the blood vessels can sometimes be repaired surgically.

What can go wrong with the nerves that control erection?

The most important function of the nervous system in bringing about an erection is to stimulate the arteries to expand and allow a rapid flow of blood into the penis. Anything that damages this part of the nervous system will therefore, interfere with this process and make erection difficult or impossible. There are, for example, some diseases such as diabetes or multiple sclerosis which may (though not always) affect the quality of an erection in this way. However, a more probable cause of damage to the nerves is through drug abuse, particularly alcohol, which over a long period is likely to cause considerable damage to the nervous system and interfere with erection (see pp. 30–1).

What part do the sex hormones play in producing an erection?

Hormones play a very important part in a man becoming aroused and having a good erection. The process is very complicated, but we know that there are a number of different hormones involved, although how they work together with the nervous system is not fully understood.

In the first place, there has to be enough of the male sex hormone *testosterone*, which is produced in the testes, if erection is to take place normally. If a man is castrated after puberty and his testosterone is not replaced artificially by tablets or injection, his capacity to get an erection will usually gradually decline. Likewise, if he is given drugs that lead to a 'chemical castration', he will eventually lose this capacity. Whether there is enough testosterone in the bloodstream will depend upon the presence of other hormones secreted by the *pituitary gland*, to be found just beneath the brain. Over- or under-secretion of these pituitary hormones may cause an upset in testosterone levels.

Other hormones not obviously connected with sex (such as that produced by the *thyroid gland*) may also affect sexual responses. Since the *endocrine (hormone) system* of the body works together as an integrated whole, any change in the levels of one hormone can lead to upsets in others.

What is the main psychological reason why a man fails to achieve an erection?

If, for any reason, a man fails to get a good erection on a particular occasion, he may start worrying. Then, even if the events that caused the problem in the first place go away, his anxiety may remain, and as a result his worries about not getting a good erection causes just that. This then becomes a vicious circle: he worries because he cannot be sure that he will get a good erection, and he does not get a good erection because he is worrying . . . This state of affairs is known as 'performance anxiety' and plays an important part in most instances of erectile loss.

What other kinds of stress can lead to erection failure?

Various events can trigger erectile problems. Perhaps the most important are problems that arise from the relationship with one's partner. Most of us desire to please our partners when we make love, and this is fine, as long as these desires do not get out of hand. If they do, a man can then find himself becoming a victim to these desires – he wants to please so much and becomes so concerned about his ability to perform that the stress that results causes him to lose the ability to achieve an erection. He then ceases to be able to respond to his partner in a positive and assertive manner. This lack of confidence in himself will lead him to feel rejected and unloved, not the ideal mood for making love effectively.

A man may also lose his erection because he is no longer aroused sexually by his partner; she may, for example, have taken on (either temporarily or permanently) the role of a mother figure, or he may have become bored with their love-making because it is so frequent or repetitive. He may simply have fallen out of love with her – or fallen in love with someone else. He may not get an erection (or allow himself to do so) because he is angry with her or because, in his eyes, she is too demanding sexually or not responsive enough. Because of space restrictions, these explanations are necessarily simplistic. It is clear that the part played by relationships is very complex, and often only a skilled counsellor can unravel all the causes and help solve the problem.

In addition, most people have day-to-day worries. Indeed, there are few who, at some time or other, have not had anxious moments about money, housing, health, work, children and other family matters. These lifestyle problems usually sort themselves out, but while they are still present, they can have an effect on a person's sex life. Men, as well as women, may find that they are not interested in making love, which, for men, may mean they have difficulty in achieving erections.

Which are more important in the loss of erections – physical or psychological causes?

It is impossible to say which of the two, the physical or psychological, is more important because both sets of causes are usually involved to some extent. Statistical evidence is also somewhat suspect because the information obtained can be biased depending upon from where it comes. For instance, you would expect to find rather more men with a physical basis to their impotence from a sample of patients who attended a hospital clinic specializing in the medical treatment of erectile dysfunction than in those who had consulted, say, Relate (formerly the National Marriage Guidance Council see p. 148), which specializes in the use of psychological treatments. However, even allowing for the inevitable guesswork it is probably true to say that both physical and psychological causes are probably roughly evenly balanced in importance.

How do specialists in sexual medicine decide whether the causes of erectile problems are largely physical or psychological?

Men with erectile problems often believe that their problems are physical in origin and have a medical solution; doctors, on the other hand, frequently think that their patients' problems are psychological and that they need counselling or psychotherapy. Clearly, this situation is unsatisfactory since the outcome of such a decision will influence the kind of treatment offered. Specialists require answers to a number of questions, and only when these have been established will they be able to make an informed guess as to whether a particular problem is largely physical or psychological in origin.

To interpret the table, add up the scores for the four main causes – P (psychological), V (blood supply), H (hormonal), N (nerve supply) – scoring one for each capital letter (e.g. P=1, PP=2, etc.). If the total score of V + H + N exceeds the total P score, there is a strong suggestion that there may be a physical (medical) cause for the erectile dysfunction. If, on the other hand, the total P score exceeds that of V + H + N, a psychological explanation must be considered. If the two sets of scores are roughly balanced (differing by 2 or 3 either way), no firm conclusion can be arrived at. The individual totals of V, H and N scores may provide a pointer to which particular physical cause (if any) is responsible.

The questionnaire on pp. 24–6 is designed *only* to provide readers with a very rough idea of the main causes for their possible erectile difficulties and how these might be identified by a specialist in sexual medicine; it is *not* meant to offer a reliable means of self-diagnosis. It is very important to seek professional advice if you are concerned about this sort of problem.

Go through the questionnaire, answering 'yes' or 'no' to the various items. After you have answered the questions, circle the letter or letters beside the answer.

You may not be able to answer all the questions, but this does not matter.

A guide to the main causes of erectile loss

Note: A few of these questions, marked with an asterisk can only be answered after the results of further investigations are available.

Possible cause: P = psychological V = blood supply
H = hormonal N = nerve supply

		P	V	H	N
Maximum scores:		(24)	(16)	(8)	(12)
1.	Has the problem with erection always been present?	YES	V	H	N
2.	Are rigid erections easily obtained by self-masturbation?	YES P / NO	V	H	N
3.	Are rigid, persistent morning erections regularly present – i.e at least once a week?	YES P			
4.	Is there an overwhelming feeling of performance anxiety, a fear of sexual failure?	YES P			
5.	Are there any known relevant health problems (see pp. 33–7)?	YES	V	H	N
6.	Is erection lost at or immediately after penetration during intercourse, but not at other times?	YES P			
7.	Is erection lost with some partners but not with others?	YES P			
8.	Is erection lost in some situations but not in others with the same partner?	YES P			
9.	Has there been a loss of partner through divorce, bereavement or rejection?	YES PP			
10.	Is there a history of depression preceding the erectile loss?	YES PP			
11.	Is there a history of psychiatric problems requiring hospitalization?	YES P			
12.	Are there problems within the relationship (if any)?	YES PP			

13.	Are there serious lifestyle problems (e.g. work, money, housing, etc.)?	YES	P	
14.	Do you have an over-anxious personality and/or are you obsessional (i.e. excessively tidy, clean, punctual and strict)?	YES	PP	
15.	Was there a lot of stress and trauma in childhood?	YES	P	
16.	Are rigid, traditional and moral attitudes a feature of your personality?	YES	PP	
17.	Is there a history of homosexual behaviour?	YES	P	
18.	Are you aged over 60?	YES	P	V
19.	Are your sexual fantasies at masturbation unusual (e.g. sadistic, masochistic, fetishistic, etc.)?	YES	P	
20.	Are there any physical clues – e.g. small testes, marked presence of breast tissue, female body shape?	YES		H
21.	When investigated, were unusual hormone levels discovered?*	YES		HH
22.	Have you been prescribed any medicines containing hormones recently?	YES		H
23.	Have you been prescribed any other medication, likely to cause a loss of, erection (see p. 31)?	YES		V	N
24.	Have you had any recent surgical operations in the pelvic region (other than to repair a hernia)?	YES			N
25.	Have you had any injuries to or operations on your back?	YES			N
26.	Do you experience any difficulties controlling urination?	YES	P		N
27.	Is there a history of high blood pressure, heart disease or stroke?	YES		VV	N
28.	*Do specialized neurological (nerve) tests reveal any abnormalities?	YES			NN
29.	Is there a history of poor circulation, cold fingers or feet				

and, particularly, a cold penis?	YES	V		
30. Does the penis bend in the middle or change in colour on erection?	YES	V		
31. Has a programme of properly supervised *sensate focus* (see pp. 40–44) been completed unsuccessfully?	YES	V	H	N
32. *Is a good erection obtained after an injection of papaverine (p. 27) into the penis?	NO	VV		
33. *Do specialized tests reveal problems with blood flow in the penis?	YES	VV		
34. Is there a loss of erection on standing or changing position?	YES	V		
35. *Is the blood pressure in the penis low?	YES	V		

If the causes of the erectile failure are thought to be largely physical, what happens then?

First, you will be referred to a hospital or medical centre where a consultant specializing in the treatment of erectile problems will be able to conduct some tests. Normally, this will be a urologist (sometimes known as an *andrologist*, the male equivalent of a gynaecologist), who is a medically qualified specialist who treats disorders of the male urinary and reproductive system. Urologists have at their disposal facilities to pursue more exacting investigations that would not be available elsewhere. You may, however, be examined by a psychiatrist (also medically qualified) who specializes in sexual medicine.

Blood will be taken and tested, and other investigations will measure the ease with which the blood flows into the penis. The nerve supply to the genital region will also be monitored. Armed with the results of these tests, the urologist will be able to say, with some confidence, whether or not he believes that physical factors have contributed significantly to the loss of erection.

Are these tests available on the NHS?

Yes: every health region will have at least one
specialist clinic where these tests are available, but the
waiting period may be quite long – sometimes months.
However, most private hospitals will be able to do
these tests within a week or so, although the cost can
be quite substantial. Private medical insurance will
normally cover the cost of these investigations.

Is it true that injections into the penis can cure problems with erection?

Recently, it has been shown that substances injected
(using a syringe with a very fine, short needle) directly
into the shaft of the penis will provide an immediate
erection in men who otherwise would be unable to get
one. After instruction, men can even inject themselves
at home. Surprisingly, these injections are quite
painless.

There are several substances that will produce this
response, but *papaverine* and *phentolamine* are those
most widely used. They act simply by dilating the
arteries that feed blood into the penis; an erection
usually follows as a result. Urologists will often use
papaverine early on in their investigations to help
them find out what is causing the erectile problem.

If a man has failed to get an erection for some time
but gets a good response following a single injection of
papaverine, this means that the problem is either
psychological (because papaverine will dilate the
arteries feeding the penis no matter how the man feels
about his performance or his partner) or, more likely,
neurological: that is, there is a disease affecting the
nerve supply to the penis since the expansion of the
blood vessels in the penis will still take place after an
injection of papaverine even if the nerve supply is not
functioning.

However, if, following an injection of papaverine, the
man still fails to get a good erection, this would
suggest that there is something wrong with the blood

supply to the penis – such as a venous leak (see p. 19) – because papaverine, despite its many beneficial qualities, cannot repair holes and leaks in the blood vessels.

Does papaverine produce any harmful side-effects?

Normally, no. However, very occasionally the resulting erection will not go away – a condition called *priapism*, which can be harmful. If an erection persists for longer than about four hours, the erectile tissue can be permanently damaged so that any further erection is then impossible. Urologists who treat patients with papaverine will forewarn them about the possibility of priapism and ensure that they know where to go for emergency treatment. Normally a further injection into the penis of *phenylephrine*, a substance that constricts the arteries, will solve the problem. However, a word of caution: this use of papaverine is a new technique, and so far, there has not been time to establish for certain whether, apart from priapism, any other harmful side-effects may arise from its prolonged use.

Will hormone injections help?

It is widely believed that injections of sex hormones will work miracles on those with erectile problems. Advertisements appear in the media, men with these difficulties clamour for this 'wonder' cure and hard-pressed doctors give patients jabs in their bottoms – but to little effect. The truth is that very few erectile problems are caused by low levels of the sex hormone testosterone, mainly responsible for normal sexual functioning. For this reason, and because too much testosterone can be as harmful as too little, no one should ever be given hormones regularly either by injection or tablet until he has had a blood test that reveals a low testosterone level. Then, and only then, would hormone replacement be called for. More often, the testosterone level is not abnormal – and the specialist has to look elsewhere for an explanation.

What effect does high blood pressure have on the process of erection?

For reasons that are not fully understood, high blood pressure seems to cause problems with erection. However, it may be that other factors – such as the hardening of the arteries (arteriosclerosis) – are the real culprits, and the discovery of high blood pressure is one way of detecting that something else is wrong.

Why do men, even those with erectile difficulties, sometimes find that they regularly have erections on waking?

Many men under the age of 50 report that, about once or twice a week, they wake with an erection. An erection at this time is not, as is commonly supposed, caused by a full bladder, but is instead the last of a number of so-called 'sleep erections' that have been occurring throughout the night. Most men will have spontaneous erections when they are in the very shallow dream sleep known as 'rapid eye movement', or 'REM', sleep – so described because the eyes are actively moving as the person dreams. Men will only notice these erections if they wake up during this period of shallow REM sleep.

These morning and night erections are significant because they can provide some information about whether the physiology of erection is working normally. A man who regularly awakes with a hard and rigid erection that does not disappear immediately when he stands up is unlikely to have anything seriously wrong with him physically. If he is failing to get erections when attempting intercourse, the chances are that his problem has a psychological cause.

Because this kind of test is useful, a way of testing the frequency of these night-time REM erections has been devised. Two mercury 'strain gauges' are attached to the top and the bottom of the penis before the man goes to sleep. These gauges are themselves attached to a monitoring device, which then records any change in the diameter of the penis. If it is discovered that REM erections are absent, there may be a physical cause to the problem; if they are shown to be present, this would suggest that the causes may be psychological. However, the test is not foolproof by any means, particularly since the strain gauges do not measure the *rigidity* of the penis, which is an essential ingredient of a good erection. Despite this drawback, the test is perfectly harmless, and it may provide some additional information that will help the specialist to arrive at an appropriate diagnosis.

What effect does alcohol have on erections?

The obvious effects of drinking on sexual enjoyment and performance are well known to most men. By reducing inhibitions and, therefore, feelings of anxiety, small quantities of alcohol can increase emotional and sexual interest. Modest amounts of alcohol can also improve the quality of love-making because it helps both men and women to 'let go'.

However, alcohol is not a wonder drug, nor is it an aphrodisiac. The immediate effects of drinking too much is that, first, a man will notice that his penis becomes less sensitive and, second, he loses the capacity to get or maintain an erection. However, individuals vary quite incredibly in the way they respond to alcohol: some men find it difficult to get an erection after only two or three pints of beer, whereas others seem to be quite unaffected and even claim improved performance after ten pints!

The long-term effects of sustained alcohol abuse are much more dangerous and sometimes irreversible. Regular heavy drinking over a number of years will damage many organs, but particularly the liver and the nervous system. Alcohol is a poison. In large quantities, it acts directly upon the body tissues, and it also leads to vitamin deficiencies that may damage the nerves. The amount of alcohol that has to be consumed to produce this damage will vary from person to person. However, if a man drinks an average of six or seven pints of beer or a third of a bottle of spirits a day over a period of years, he will stand a good chance of permanently losing his ability to get an erection – not to mention permanently damaging his liver.

Are there are regularly prescribed medicines that will make erections difficult to achieve?

The process of erection is very susceptible to many of the modern drugs that are now regularly prescribed by doctors. For this reason, if a man notices a sudden deterioration in the quality of his erection, which also coincides with the beginning of a new course of medication, it would be very wise for him to see his doctor immediately. He can then find out whether the drugs that he is taking are responsible. If the medication is playing a part, it can perhaps be changed, but if not, at least he will know the reason and not look elsewhere for an explanation.

Some of the stronger, morphine-based painkillers can affect erection, as can some commonly prescribed tranquillizers and sleeping tablets, particularly if they are taken over a long period. Anti-depressants can also be singled out as serious offenders. Drugs prescribed for high blood pressure and heart disease are notorious for their bad effects on erection; there are now, however, a number of alternatives available that can be tried and which, for some men at least, do not appear to have any effect on erection – in fact, some may even improve erections. Hormones are prescribed for a number of conditions – for example, oestrogens (female sex hormones) – for some cancers – and, understandably, these may interfere with erection. Drugs used in the treatment of epilepsy will not normally affect erection adversely, particularly if they are taken in low doses, but when a high dosage is required, erection failure can occur.

Do remedies such as Vitamin E or ginseng help?
There is no evidence that vitamin supplements or
herbal preparations of any sort will improve a man's
ability to get an erection – to put it bluntly, they are a
waste of money. Naturally, one can never eliminate the
so-called 'placebo effect' – that is, if you believe in
something, it will work – but if there were any preparations that were guaranteed to produce the desired
effects, the discoverer would be a millionaire by now.

**Some men put a tight rubber ring around the base
of the penis to prevent loss of erection. Is this
dangerous?**
As long as the ring is not too tight, it will do no harm,
but it may not do much good either. Rubber rings and
the vulcanite-and-metal Blakoe rings that encircle the
base of the penis and the scrotum probably only work
because of the placebo effect, but there is no harm in
trying them because some men claim that these rings
do help them keep an erection.

**Are there any artificial aids that might help a man
get or keep an erection?**
For those men for whom other methods of treatment
have failed, there remains the opportunity to have a
penile implant, or *penile splint* inserted. There are two
main types: one comprises a pair of silicone or silastic
rods that are inserted surgically into the penis to
produce a permanent erection; the other consists of an
inflatable tube into which fluid contained in a reservoir
inserted surgically in the lower abdomen in front of the
bladder can be pumped in and out to produce an
erection when wanted.

However simple and effective it sounds, a man
should think carefully before he decides to have an
implant because, once it has been inserted, the erectile
tissue is permanently destroyed and a natural erection
will never again be possible. Complications such as
recurrent infections can also arise, and it has even

been reported that the rods can poke through the end of the penis after particularly vigorous sexual activity.

In addition, all types of these implants are very expensive. This means that private treatment would be beyond the means of most, and many NHS clinics ration these implants for financial reasons.

So-called 'vacuum condoms' are advertised as a cure for erectile problems. Are they worth trying?
Recently, a device called the *Corectaid* has been on sale in the United States and elsewhere, complete with a money-back guarantee. It works on a very simple principle: a condom is placed over the flaccid penis and secured firmly at the base; air is then removed from within it by sucking on a tube attached to the condom; the partial vacuum so created encourages blood to flow into the penis, and the penis then becomes erect; once an adequate erection is obtained, the partial vacuum is retained by winding the tube around the base of the penis. Some men report that it works very well, although there will be considerable loss of sensitivity because the material from which the condom is made has to be quite thick.

Another device called the *ErecAid* uses a hand vacuum pump attached to a glass condom, which is fitted over the limp penis; the condom is removed when an erection is obtained. Penetration then occurs without the device in place, which is an obvious advantage. The erection is maintained by a rubber ring that is slipped off the end of the device on to the base of the penis.

Both these vacuum condoms cost about £250 (1989 prices).

What diseases are likely to cause problems with erection?
Most bodily functions will work less well when a person becomes ill. Apart from common acute illnesses such as flu, which lay sufferers up for a week or so and

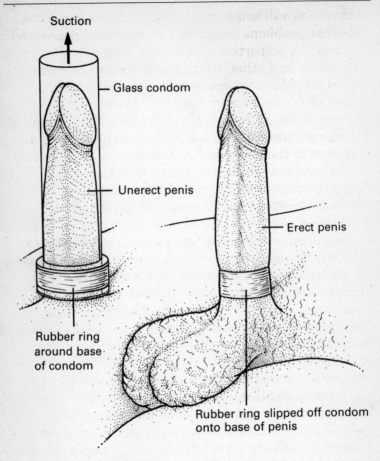

Suction

Glass condom

Unerect penis

Erect penis

Rubber ring
around base
of condom

Rubber ring slipped off condom
onto base of penis

The *ErecAid* vacuum condom

sex is naturally the last thing on their mind, there are
also a large number of chronic diseases, injuries and
surgical procedures that can affect sexual performance
and particularly erection:

Anorexia nervosa ('slimmer's disease') Although
anorexia is characteristically a disease of young
women, it can also affect men. In both sexes, it has a
devastating effect upon their sex lives.
*Cardiovascular disease (e.g. heart attack, high blood
pressure and stroke)* Diseases affecting the circulation

of the blood will sometimes affect sexual performance.
Often the problems are caused by the drugs prescribed.

Diabetes   A proportion of men will have erectile
difficulties, and other sexual problems will occur in
both sexes. Many diabetics, however, will have no
sexual problems whatsoever.

Diseases affecting hormone production   There are a
number of diseases that may affect the production and
operation of the endocrine (hormone) system. An upset
of this kind may influence sexual behaviour.

Epilepsy   Sexual problems are frequent but not
inevitable. Sometimes they are caused by the
medication required.

Kidney disease   Sexual problems are very common in
men and women with kidney disease, and even when
they have regular dialysis, improvement is not
guaranteed. Transplantation, however, often brings
some amelioration.

Multiple sclerosis   Erectile problems in men, together
with other sexual problems in both sexes, are often
found in those with MS.

'Ostomies'   Sometimes it is necessary to have part of
the large or small intestine removed, either because of
an inflammatory disease or because of cancer. It is
then usually necessary to create an artificial opening –
a *stoma* – in the abdomen to allow solid waste to
escape into a bag. These operations are known as
colostomies and *ileostomies*, depending on which part of
the intestines is removed. As a result of these surgical
procedures, the nerves serving the sexual organs are
sometimes damaged, and there is then a loss of sexual
function.

Peyronies disease   In this condition, hard patches of
tissue develop in the shaft of the penis. This results in
partial, painful erections, and also sometimes a curving
of the penis when it is erect.

Prostate gland operations (prostatectomy)   A majority
of men over the age of 50 will have an enlarged
prostate gland, the organ that is responsible for

providing some of the semen (the remainder coming from the *seminal vesicles*). Normally this enlargement presents no problems, but about 10 per cent of these men may experience difficulties passing urine. If this happens, minor surgery is usually required, which normally has little or no effect on sexual performance. When, more rarely, the prostate gland becomes cancerous and has to be removed altogether, there may be a greater loss of sexual function, although often this only results in a loss of ejaculation and not of erection.

Psychiatric illness　It is often difficult to separate the effects of some types of mental illnesses, such as severe depression or schizophrenia, on sexual behaviour from the effects of the medication that is so often prescribed for these conditions. Although most anti-depressants and anti-psychotic drugs prescribed for depression and schizophrenia will probably slow down sexual responses, the illnesses themselves will also affect sexual performance – in particular, those suffering from depression often say they have lost interest in sex, even without medication. Schizophrenics, on the other hand, are more unpredictable, and although their illness may affect their sexual performance (making it either stronger or weaker), it is usually the side-effects of the drugs they are taking which are responsible for any sexual problem they may have.

Spinal injuries　Injuries to the spine that result in an interruption of the nerve supply from the genitals to the brain will obviously affect sexual function. Depending upon the position and type of injury, a man's ability to get an erection and ejaculate may be either partially or seriously affected.

It is important to remember that even if a man does suffer from one of these conditions, he will not necessarily have difficulty getting an erection. Individuals vary considerably in their response to disease, and of course, worrying about the effects of being ill can sometimes be worse than the effects of the illness itself. Finally, it must be stressed that if a man believes that his problems with erection are caused by ill health, it is essential that he consults a medical practitioner as soon as possible.

Why can some men get an erection in a new relationship but can no longer do so with their regular partners?

The explanation that obviously comes to mind is that the excitement and novelty associated with a new partner may well enable a man who is no longer aroused by his regular partner to get an erection. However, while there is no doubt that many husbands do get bored – or 'habituated' as psychologists would call it – with their wives (as do wives with their husbands), this is more likely to lead to a refusal to have intercourse than to a loss of erection.

A more probable reason for this phenomenon is that some men find it extremely difficult to express both their sexual feelings *and* their loving feelings to the same person. This conflict between sex and love is probably present to some degree in most people; psychoanalysts have even given it a name – for men, it is the 'princess/prostitute syndrome'. It probably stems from the difficulty that boys in particular have in separating themselves emotionally from their mothers. If these so-called 'incestuous' feelings persist throughout life, as they do in some, they will create havoc with the relationships of these men and prevent them settling down. Difficulties arise, sooner or later, when their girlfriends become their wives and, finally, the mothers of their children. However attractive and desirable these women remain, affected men find sex with them difficult if not impossible because the women are then seen as mother figures. For these men, a purely physical relationship with another woman such as a prostitute provides the only opportunity for a really rewarding sexual encounter, however sordid, risky and expensive this may be, because she remains, at least in the short term, very unmotherlike and sexy.

37

How does a woman feel if her partner is unable to get an erection when they make love?

At least in a new relationship one of the nicest compliments anyone can pay their sexual partner is to become aroused. If necessary a woman can pretend to be 'turned on', but a man cannot because if he does not get an erection this cannot easily be disguised. Most sexually active women will have experienced occasions when their partners have been unable to get an erection, the reasons for this being quite obvious at the time. Fatigue, alcohol, fear of interruption or a relationship mismatch are some of the reasons why this might happen. Sometimes, however, there does not appear to be any obvious explanation and this will leave the woman very confused. She will feel hurt, rejected, unloved and perhaps even unlovable. These feelings may amount only to disappointment or she may be angry and humiliated, particularly if in a stable relationship she comes to the conclusion that her partner has met someone else.

Whatever her feelings, she must not take this personally and blame herself. It is not *her* fault if *he* cannot get an erection, and there may be absolutely nothing she can do about it. It may be that they are simply not suited to each other sexually, or he may have had the same problem with other partners. One thing is certain, he will be in a better position to know why he is not getting an erection than she ever will. However, if both are prepared to talk honestly to each other it is usually quite easy to discover what is wrong and if communication between them is difficult then the intervention of a therapist can help considerably. To say that he must take responsibility for his erection does not mean that she should wash her hands of the whole business (unless she wants to). Instead, they should try to work together to find out what is wrong and then put it right if they can.

**How important is it to get a man's relationship
with his partner right before he begins treatment
for an erectile problem?**

Treating men with erectile problems probably presents
sex therapists with their most difficult challenge. Even
when physical causes have been eliminated as a major
factor and the therapist is fairly certain that the 'psychology' of the situation is of paramount importance,
there are still many problems to disentangle.

It is most likely that the man's partner will be
involved in the story and so, if therapy is to be
successful, it must involve her. If, however, the
relationship has little prospect of surviving, or it is
clear that his partner will not agree to join therapy,
alternatives will have to be discussed. One thing is
clear: it is almost impossible to undertake most forms
of sex therapy without a partner. But, of course, it is
not usually enough just to have any partner. If therapy
is to be of any use, the woman must really want it to
work and must become involved with her partner so
that they can work together. Moreover, he needs to
know that she really cares and is not just going
through the motions. In practice, these conditions are
not always easily met, for the simple reason that it is
often a breakdown in the relationship that has led to
the erectile problem in the first place.

However, there is little point in getting down to the
details of a sex therapy programme unless and until a
couple feel that they can communicate and understand
one another's needs, and unless the woman in
particular can willingly involve herself in treatment.
So, before starting any sex therapy, the therapist must
spend some time helping the couple to try to achieve
some degree of closeness and understanding of each
other's needs. This is not an easy task and it may take
several visits, but an essential part of this kind of
marital therapy is to try to help the couple to be honest
with each other however hurtful it may seem at the
time. Sometimes such therapy fails because one or

other cannot live with what they discover about their relationship (although, usually, they will have dropped out of treatment before this point is reached). More often, it works because much of the anger and resentment and misunderstandings that have been bottled up are now released and the relationship benefits as a result. If possible it is helpful to try to keep a sense of humour throughout and not take things too seriously.

Once the therapist feels that the couple are close enough to start the practical side of therapy, he will explain in more detail a sex therapy programme which will probably be largely based on the ideas of American sex therapists Masters and Johnson[4]. Details of this are described next.

How are problems with erection of 'psychological' origin usually treated?

One of the best ways to begin therapy is to introduce the couple to a form of treatment known as *sensate focus* – that is, focusing on feelings and sensations. The idea behind this is to help them become relaxed with each other both physically and mentally so that they can begin to recognize and enjoy their sexual feelings. It is used for all sorts of sexual problems, of both men and women.

In order to remove any sense of anxiety or pressure or what are known as 'performance fears', the couple agree to a ban on intercourse for an initial period of, say, four weeks (it may be longer or shorter, depending upon circumstances). They should also agree that this is an undertaking that should always be observed and taken seriously. In addition, it is important that they try to arrange their lives so that they can occasionally be alone, without fear of interruption. They need a period of about an hour or so twice a week when they are not too tired, irritable or pressured by time.

Sensate focus begins with the couple 'pleasuring' each other. This means that they *take it in turns* to explore slowly and gently each other's body by caressing and massaging in such a way that each in turn can totally relax and focus on the feelings that they experience as they are being touched by their partner.

Touch is a very important means of communication between people and one that is very often neglected in our high-tech society. The success of sensate focus depends very much on being able to relax and concentrate on the feelings and sensations experienced through touch. No one need talk unless compelled to do so except on those occasions when it might perhaps be helpful for one partner to tell the other when and where a caress is particularly rewarding, or when it is not.

The couple have also agreed that, during the early stages of sensate focus, neither should touch the other's genitals – in other words, the penis and the vulva (comprising the clitoris, the fatty skin folds known as labia, and the opening of the vagina). Otherwise, anything goes: the touch can be gentle or firm, and the whole body can be explored in whatever way is enjoyed most. It is a very good idea to use some body cream, baby oil or talc, but even this is not essential if, for one reason or another, it does not add to the pleasure.

One way to start sensate focus is to begin to massage your partner while he/she is lying on his/her stomach. Stroking and caressing can begin on the legs, arms or neck and then move to the back and bottom, finishing perhaps on the insides of the thighs, which are particularly sensitive and sexy for most people. Then, after your partner turns over, you can begin again on his/her chest or breasts, arms, legs and then the abdomen. Pleasuring can end by kissing and cuddling, but the penis and vulva must not be touched nor should intercourse be attempted at this stage.

After two or three sessions in which relaxation, sensory pleasure and moderate sexual arousal is enjoyed, the penis will usually have begun to get erect from time to time. It may have happened on the first occasion or it may take a little while longer. If, by any chance, an erection does not come after two or three weeks, it may be that the couple are still not ready for sensate focus and that there still remains a need for further counselling with the therapist.

For the older man – say, over the age of 50 – erections may take longer to appear, and a first erection may not be possible without some direct stimulation to the penis. However, it is still important to observe the ban on touching the genitals, at least for the first three or four sessions. Then, and only then can the penis be stimulated directly.

Once a spontaneous erection begins to come naturally during sensate focus, the partners can gently stimulate each other's penis and vulva, using hands. This does not mean vigorous, mutual masturbation but, as before, taking it in turns to allow the other to focus on the feelings in the genitals. It must be remembered that each partner is giving to the other – one is relaxed and focusing on the feelings produced by the other – and that, throughout sensate focus, all the sex play is non-demanding. In other words, it requires no response from the partner, nor is there any need to achieve any particular goal.

Once an erection becomes a normal feature of sensate focus, it is a good idea for the man to allow himself to deliberately lose his erection and then regain it. In this way, he will be reassured that, if he does lose his erection when making love, he can usually get it back.

Towards the final stages of the sensate focus programme, the couple can gently begin simultaneous pleasuring until they are both ready for penetration. The best way to attempt this is for the man to lie on his back with his penis erect and pointing upwards. His partner will then gently lower herself on him, directing his penis into her vagina with her hand. She can then move very slowly up and down while remaining on top of him. It is a very good idea to make sure that her vulva and vagina are moist when penetration is first attempted; if they are not, plenty of cream or oil or a special non-greasy lubricant such as KY jelly should be used.

It does not really matter whether the man ejaculates or not at this stage, although he should not deliberately try to stop himself. In fact, in these early stages of intercourse it is probably best to allow the woman to move just sufficiently for her partner to hold his erection. Likewise, it is not going to help if she tries to stimulate herself to orgasm because orgasm-seeking will just put both partners under pressure to perform and may raise anxieties. At this point, all that is required is for the man to begin to enjoy the feeling in his penis when it is inside the woman's vagina.

As his confidence increases, so different positions of intercourse can be tried. However, sex play should always remain a very important part of love-making, and there is no reason why a couple should not return to the earlier stages of sensate focus in order to recapture the unique feelings of being relaxed and able to enjoy their own bodies.

If at any stage there is a setback and the man loses the ability to achieve erection (not an unlikely event), all that needs to be done is to go back to an earlier stage in the sensate focus programme. He should not be too worried about what has happened. Partial or total loss of erection during love play and intercourse is a common occurrence for every man, so no significance should be attached to it.

Sometimes sensate focus does not seem to work very well, and a couple give up. However, it is most important to stay with the programme for about three or four weeks at least. Then, if there is no progress at all, it may mean that the couple are temperamentally unsuited to this kind of approach and one or more of three following approaches might be tried.

Sometimes a man will get an erection early in a

sensate focus session, lose it almost immediately as pleasuring proceeds and then find it very difficult to get it back, however relaxed he is. If this happens regularly, it is sometimes worthwhile taking advantage of the first erection and attempting intercourse immediately. However, it must be stressed that this instruction is not here to tempt the majority to dispense with sensate focus but is only suggested for those who have tried sensate focus but the programme clearly does not work for them.

During sensate focus, the mind must be totally relaxed and tuned into bodily sensations. Some men find this very difficult and cannot relax sufficiently to shut out their performance fears. They engage in what is described as 'spectatoring', when they mentally monitor the size of their penis and become totally preoccupied with their lack of response. Not surprisingly, this habit becomes a self-fulfilling prophecy and must be stopped if sensate focus is to succeed.

One way to achieve this is for the couple to take a shower together: the effect of the water (the more powerful the jets the better) acts as a form of distraction and can work wonders. Alternatively, the couple could try having a bath or taking a jacuzzi together. Indeed, there are a whole range of different 'distraction' strategies that can be tried if sensate focus fails. For example, a mock fight can be arousing, and the use of a male vibrator on the penis and even the man masturbating his partner to orgasm may distract him sufficiently to allow an erection. However, relaxation is more likely to work in the majority of cases.

Does sensate focus treatment work?
Published figures on the success of sensate focus programmes, when used for the treatment of erectile dysfunction, are not particularly helpful since they vary so much. The best results come from the United

States where Masters and Johnson obtained a 75 per cent success rate[5], but sex therapists in the United Kingdom report successes only of the order of 25 to 30 per cent[6].

These relatively poor results can probably be explained by the fact that sadly, many couples, do not seek treatment until their relationships have deteriorated almost beyond repair, with sex as one of the main casualties. It is not surprising, therefore, that the type of commitment required for the success of sensate focus is often not present. A further problem is that sometimes physical causes for erectile difficulties are missed; clearly, the use of these psychological methods are less likely to be effective in these instances.

How does a sex therapist help someone who has a sexual problem such as loss of erection but does not have a partner?

It is obviously very difficult, if not impossible, to provide any effective sex therapy for someone who does not have a partner. Individuals who have a disabling sexual problem are in a 'Catch 22' situation: they cannot establish a relationship because of the problem, yet they need a relationship if they are to be able to deal with it.

One way round this is to use 'surrogate therapy'. The word 'surrogate' means 'substitute', and in sex therapy, a surrogate partner is a man or woman who is prepared to act as a sexual partner to those who need help with sexual problems. Surrogate therapy is not widely available in the UK. However, one of the authors[7] has, for many years arranged for his partnerless clients to take advantage of this special form of sex therapy, and although it has not been easy to organize, the results obtained have certainly justified the effort.

3.
PREMATURE EJACULATION

To be able to postpone ejaculation as long as they wish during intercourse is a desire almost universally held by men. For some, however, this capacity to delay ejaculation is not always possible, and many of those who continually reach orgasm and ejaculate perhaps within a minute of penetration become deeply distressed. Without claiming miracles, sex therapists can provide some help, although success does depend upon the commitment and cooperation of both the man and his partner.

What is premature ejaculation?
Premature ejaculation, perhaps better described as 'quick ejaculation', is the response of those men who reach organism very quickly, via either masturbation or intercourse. It is impossible to define precisely the problem of quick ejaculation because, for some couples, it does not present any difficulties. If a man maintains an erection for only two or three minutes after penetration, this may be quite acceptable to some women, although it may be distressing to others. However, there are some men who, for various reasons, either ejaculate before they have penetrated the vagina or very shortly afterwards – so that intercourse lasts only a few seconds. It is important, therefore, to try to restrict the use of the description 'premature ejaculation' only to those situations where one or other (or both) of the partners is clearly distressed.

How long does intercourse last, on average?

It is very difficult to give an accurate answer to this question. In the first place, length of intercourse varies from day to day, and second, measurement of the passage of time becomes distorted when one is sexually aroused. Kinsey, in his surveys[8], found that about one in three men ejaculated within two minutes of beginning intercourse, but not all investigations have produced the same results, and others have suggested that the average man may last for at least twice that time[9]. However, without a stopwatch by the bedside and a decision in advance to time intercourse (a decision that might itself change things anyway), all estimates are going to be very unreliable.

This is, however, a very important question, and it is probably safe to say that, except in the young and in those in new relationships, the length of intercourse is not usually much longer than 10–15 minutes, and for the majority, it is quite a brief affair, usually lasting less than five minutes. In this case, a man who can postpone orgasm for three minutes is hardly justified in describing himself a 'premature ejaculator'.

How common is it?

Difficulties with erection and quick ejaculation are the two most frequently experienced problems in men. Generally speaking, difficulties with erection appear to outnumber problems with ejaculation, but this may be because quick ejaculation is better tolerated by couples than loss of erection. About 25 per cent of men seeking help at sex problem clinics complain of premature ejaculation[10], although any attempt to estimate the percentage of the male population who ejaculate quickly would inevitably involve a wild guess.

How do men ejaculate?

The ejaculation of the semen (the milky fluid containing the sperm) at orgasm is a reflex rather like a sneeze or a cough, and like sneezing or coughing, there is a vast individual variation in sensitivity to stimulation. Some men will have a very sensitive, 'hair trigger' ejaculatory reflex, whereas others require much more stimulation before they become aroused and ejaculate. Indeed, rarely, some men cannot ejaculate at all (see Chapter 4).

The process of ejaculation occurs in two stages – the first is quite involuntary, the second is partly under the man's control. *Stage 1* is the contraction of the tubes that deliver the sperm from the testes, where they are made. The *prostate gland* and a pair of sacs called the *seminal vesicles*, all of which contribute to the semen in which the sperm are ejaculated also contract in this first stage. These contractions pump

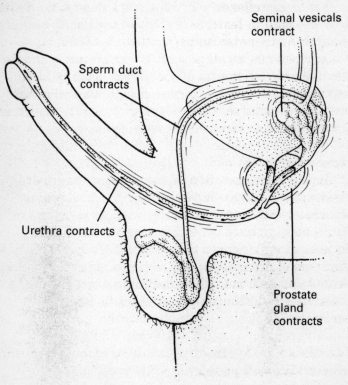

The path the sperm take from the testes to the exterior at orgasm

the semen to the base of the erect penis. In *Stage 2*, muscles at the base of the penis contract rhythmically and shoot the semen through the urethra running the length of the penis, until the semen (and the sperm) reach the outside. These two stages follow one another very quickly.

What causes quick ejaculation?

There are probably both inborn and acquired, or learned, causes for quick ejaculation. Put simply, some men inherit quick ejaculatory reflexes and become sexually excited very rapidly. However, this is clearly not the whole story, since not only are there certain early experiences that will affect a man's ability to control these reflexes, but we also know that he retains some capacity to learn how to control the reflex even as an adult – otherwise, treatment would not work.

Most men can recall particular circumstances when they may have felt anxious or worried during love-making, and as a consequence, they have ejaculated early in intercourse. Clearly then, anxiety will increase the likelihood of rapid ejaculation. However, some men seem unable to postpone orgasm for very long even under ideal conditions when they are not under stress at all. For them, apart from the quick reflexes with which they may have been born, certain early experiences in childhood and even adolescence may play a part. Nobody is certain of the exact nature of these early experiences that increase the probability of quick ejaculation, although any experience that is likely to make a man feel quilty about sex or underconfident about relationships is a likely candidate.

Can a man suffer from premature ejaculation and have additional problems with erection?

Usually, but by no means always, men who ejaculate quickly do not have problems with erection. This is because the mechanisms that control erection are different from those responsible for ejaculation. However, occasionally men do report problems with both erection and early ejaculation. One of the reasons for this is that, if a man suffers from premature ejaculation for a long time, the anxiety that he experiences as a result may eventually also affect his capacity to get an erection. A further problem facing a man with severe premature ejaculation is that he does not have enough time to become fully aroused before he ejaculates, so he also fails to get a full erection.

Is premature ejaculation a sign of sexual immaturity?

The simple answer to this question is – NO. Although a lot of men worry about quick ejaculation and often feel inadequate as a result, it is not at all accurate to suggest that premature ejaculation is a sign of sexual immaturity, even if this could be defined. Quick ejaculation is part of the normal range of human sexual responses. Clearly, it can be very distressing in some situations, but nothing is gained by labelling yourself as a freak. The important thing is to seek advice as soon as possible.

Will changing partners have an effect?

Sexual problems cannot be considered in isolation, but only in the context of a relationship. While in some cases, admittedly, a problem will persist with every partner, there are circumstances where a new relationship may lead to a solution to the problem. This may be because the man feels much better about himself sexually with his new partner – he may, for example, feel less rejected, more loved or more assertive. Or the problem may disappear simply because the new partner is not concerned about the fact that intercourse does not last very long.

Does premature ejaculation improve as one gets older?

There is no doubt that, at the beginning of their sex

lives, many adolescents ejaculate very quickly.
However, as they get older, experience and greater
confidence will help them to control the time at which
they have an orgasm. However, for some men this
control does not appear to come easily, and they
continue to find it difficult to refrain from quick
ejaculation during intercourse throughout their lives.

How do women react to men who ejaculate quickly during intercourse?

Quick ejaculation is not something that normally
develops during the course of a relationship; it is
usually there from the beginning (except for those odd
occasions when it is caused by stress or fatigue).

Nowadays, most couples will have made love before
they decide to settle down permanently, and therefore
a woman will have been able to judge whether she and
her partner are suited sexually. If quick ejaculation
bothers her and if it persists for some time, she must
not assume that it will get better by itself. The couple
then have three courses of action open to them: accept
the situation, seek treatment or end the relationship.

Why is it that a man who normally ejaculates quickly during intercourse can often last a long time when he masturbates himself?

Both erection and ejaculation are reflexes – that is,
they do not normally require the participation of the
conscious mind. For example, a man who has broken
his spine and has no sensation in his lower body can
still sometimes get an erection and occasionally even
ejaculate. When a man masturbates himself, he is not
using all the centres of his brain, and the erection and
ejaculation that he enjoys are largely (though not
entirely) reflexive. When, however, he attempts
intercourse, the intimate contact with another person
and his emotional involvement switch on additional
centres in his brain, and it is this added emotional
arousal that leads to more rapid ejaculation. In

addition, in masturbation a man can go at his own pace – stop, start, do anything in fact – and he is in control and is not under any pressure to please his partner. He does not have to be concerned at all about his prowess or the other person's pleasure, or lack of it.

Why are men who ejaculate quickly more likely to have wet dreams?

Since men who ejaculate quickly during intercourse have a sensitive ejaculatory reflex, this is more likely to be triggered when they sleep – for example, when they are having an erotic dream – than in those in whom this reflex is less easily fired[11].

Does quick ejaculation affect the number of children you have?

The production of adequate numbers of healthy sperm is not affected by premature ejaculation. But men who cannot last in intercourse do appear to have slightly smaller families than average, but this is probably a result of their higher rate of divorce and separation and not to their capacity to father healthy children[12].

Are there any common medical conditions that are likely to cause premature ejaculation?

As far as is known, there are no physical or mental illnesses that cause premature ejaculation. There have been reports that infections of the prostate gland may lead to quick ejaculation, but these are unproven.

Does it help to delay ejaculation by masturbating to orgasm shortly before intercourse?

Some men use this method successfully to help them last longer during intercourse. Alternatively, some will have intercourse twice within a short period, lasting longer the secod time. Although this idea is a good one for those who are relatively young, it is not always possible for the older man since, for him, the interval between each orgasm becomes too long. However, generally speaking, regular masturbation is a good way of helping those who ejaculate quickly, and this is recommended in treatment.

What is the most suitable type of psychological treatment for premature ejaculation?

Nowadays, the most widely adopted approach is that of *behaviour therapy*, and it is the one described here. Put simply, this form of psychotherapy concentration on trying to modify or eliminate the unwanted behaviour itself, rather than exploring the causes for it.

How is premature ejaculation treated?

The satisfactory treatment of quick ejaculation, in common with all other sexual problems, requires a sympathetic, involved and motivated partner: very little can be done without her cooperation (see pp. 39–40).

One of the biggest problems met in treating quick ejaculation (and other sexual problems) is the difficulty experienced in trying to create a situation where the person with the difficulty is relaxed and sexually aroused at the same time. There is no question that if a man wants to be able to delay his ejaculation, he must be able to feel relaxed and at ease with his partner in bed. However, very often his feelings of well-being rapidly disappear during intercourse, when the need to please his partner seems to destroy any sense of sexual self-composure, with the result that he ejaculates quickly.

One way of attempting to deal with this sense of sexual insecurity and underconfidence is for the man's partner to go out of her way to play a passive and non-demanding role during sex play and intercourse. For example, some women are very active during intercourse, moving their groins rhythmically against the man's body in a thrusting manner. Both the physical and psychological consequences of this kind of behaviour can be disastrous for a man who is unsure how long he can last during intercourse. Similarly, if she is a noisy lover or, for example, verbally invites him to 'push harder', this invitation will often trigger the ejaculatory reflex. It may not be easy for her to play this more passive role, but if she can, it may make all the difference between success and failure. Eventually, as her partner becomes more confident and is able to delay ejaculation, she can resume a more active role.

Treatment first aims to help the couple put their 'problem' in perspective so that they do not regard it as a catastrophe. For example, if he can delay ejaculation during self-masturbation and perhaps during partner-masturbation, he can reassure himself that there cannot be anything seriously wrong with the mechanism that controls ejaculation. Part of his problem is that he becomes over-excited when he is physically and emotionally aroused at the point when he penetrates the vagina.

Also, one of the characteristics of men who ejaculate quickly is the way in which they often put their partners on a pedestal and subordinate themselves to them sexually. A man may have a quite strong personality in other avenues of life, but in bed, he is often over-preoccupied with pleasing his partner. Counselling is then directed towards helping him recognize this part of himself and teaching him to be more assertive.

The role of his partner also needs to be examined. Very often, a man who ejaculates quickly regards himself as being rejected sexually and emotionally, whether this is true or not. If he believes it to be so, such a belief will have a devastating effect upon his sexual response. Every attempt, therefore, should be made to help the couple communicate with each other honestly about their feelings towards each other so that he can be reassured that she does love him and wants to share her life with him.

Behaviour therapy is the practical side to the programme and is divided in to four stages.

- In the *first stage*, the couple are encouraged to begin to pleasure each other without any immediate sexual goals. This is called *sensate focus* (see pp. 40–44).
- The *second stage* is called *masturbation training*, which the man does on his own. He is told to masturbate regularly and is encouraged to fantasize about intercourse with a chosen partner. Many of the men who ejaculate quickly do not enjoy masturbation very much, and so they must be persuaded that this is an important part of the treatment programme. This exercise is important because it helps the man to recognize the sensations in his penis just before the 'point of no return'. Some sex therapists believe that men who ejaculate quickly are not very good at knowing when they are about to do so, and they need to be made increasingly aware of the feelings they have in their penis just before they ejaculate. In many cases, a man who ejaculates early during intercourse can last as long as he wishes during self- or even partner-masturbation and only ejaculates on penetration. However, whether he ejaculates quickly or not, he should practise the following.

There are two techniques used to delay ejaculation. The *squeeze technique* involves squeezing the top of the penis between the finger and thumb just below the corona (the rim) of the glans – that is, just below the head of the penis. Pressure applied there will normally block the ejaculatory reflex rather like stopping a sneeze by pressing the lip beneath one's nose. In the *stop–start* technique, the man brings himself almost to the point of ejaculation and then stops, restarting stimulation once the urge to ejaculate has gone. This should be repeated three or four times before he allows himself to ejaculate.

Using one or other, or both, of these techniques, he should eventually try to delay ejaculation for as long as 10–15 minutes. This should not prove difficult. It is important to accompany masturbation with sexy and arousing fantasies. Once this delay is achieved – say, by self-masturbation twice a week – he should repeat the exercise using KY jelly or baby oil on the penis to simulate the vagina's moistness.

- The *third stage* involves repeating the squeeze or stop–start technique, but this time, his partner will be taking part, masturbating him and maintaining close body contact. He can indicate to his partner when ejaculation is imminent but not inevitable, and then signal her to squeeze or withhold stimulation. If by any chance he ejaculates, the important thing is to enjoy the experience and not regard it as a failure. Initially, the squeeze needs to be quite hard to achieve its objective – this will not be painful, although he may temporarily lose his erection. This exercise should be repeated using KY jelly. When he can last 4–6 minutes with his

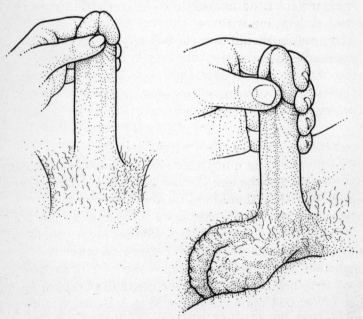

The squeeze technique used in the treatment of quick ejaculation partner, he is ready for the final stage.

- The *fourth, and final, stage* involves repeating the squeeze and/or stop–start techniques, but this time the penis is progressively introduced into the vagina. Initially, it should only be placed between the labia of the vulva, and he should ejaculate there. The next time, he should 'come' just at the entrance of the vagina, and finally, progressively, deeper penetration and ejaculation can be tried. The penis normally has to be withdrawn from the vagina so that the squeeze can be applied, although the base of penis can be squeezed instead (see diagram). Ideally, the man should be on his back in order to achieve this, but other positions can be tried to find the best one.

Once full penetration is achieved, the women on top might experiment, playing the more active role, very gently moving her body rhythmically, while the man remains passive until he is sure that there is no urgent need to ejaculate. Alternatively, he can try being on top with her playing the passive role. Each couple should experiment to establish which approach produces the best result. If there is early ejaculation, neither should worry about it but enjoy the experience since, sooner or later, some degree of control will be learned.

Does behaviour therapy work?
Men who ejaculate quickly are unlikely ever to become sexual athletes who can last for hours, but there is no reason why they should not be able to prolong intercourse with active and deep thrusting for about 2–3 minutes after treatment. If professional treatment does not help, the couple may need to become reconciled to the fact that intercourse will, of necessity, be a fairly brief affair. However, instead of regarding this as a catastrophe, they should look to other more rewarding aspects of their relationship.

Are there any drugs that will help?

It has been found, largely by accident, that some types of medication prescribed for other illnesses also have the effect of delaying ejaculation. For example, some drugs which lower blood pressure make ejaculation very difficult and sometimes impossible, and the same effect is observed in those taking some anti-depressants.

Of the latter, one in particular, which is often prescribed to help with quick ejaculation because of its effect, is *clomipramine* (trade name = Anafranil). One approach is to try a single dose of 10–25 milligrams taken about an hour before intercourse; this will normally delay ejaculation. However, clomipramine does have some side-effects, such as dizziness, and may even make erection difficult for some men. Clomipramine is only available on prescription.

Do sprays applied to the penis before intercourse work?

There are a number of types of miniature aerosol sprays that are usually available at sex shops. These contain a very small amount of a local anaesthetic which, when applied to the tip of the penis, has the effect of temporarily reducing its sensitivity and, as a result, delaying ejaculation. They are quite harmless if the instructions are followed. They work with some men but not with others.

Is there any other technique that can be tried?

Most men will have noticed that, after ejaculation, the scrotum (the skin bag containing the testes) contracts and the testes are pulled up tightly against the body instead of hanging loosely below. Because of this muscle reflex at orgasm, it has been suggested that, if a man (or his partner) gently pulls down the scrotum and testes as he approaches orgasm, this might delay ejaculation. The usefulness of this exercise, proposed by a man called Beautrais, has never been studied scientifically, but it is worth trying.

4.
DELAYED EJACULATION

Occasionally, some men find it very difficult to ejaculate at all, even after hours of stimulation. Quite apart from the distress this can cause him and his partner, there is the added problem that it may be difficult for the couple to have children. It is certainly worth seeking treatment for this condition, although the outcome will depend very much upon individual circumstances.

What is delayed ejaculation?
This is a fairly rare disorder, sometimes known as 'retarded ejaculation', in which men find it difficult to get an orgasm when aroused. Usually this only occurs during intercourse, since normally these men can ejaculate when they masturbate. However, a few men cannot ejaculate in any circumstances, and obviously this can be a very distressing problem for both them and their partners.

How common is delayed ejaculation?
When large groups of men are asked whether they have ever experienced difficulties having an orgasm and ejaculating, the answers they give will depend upon how they interpret the question. For example, various researchers[13] have found that as many as one in 20 men report that they have experienced difficulties with ejaculation on at least one occasion.

However, less than one in a 100 men probably regard this as a real problem deserving treatment.

What causes delayed ejaculation?

Sometimes the explanation is fairly clearcut, when an injury or an operation resulting in nerve damage can be held responsible. Occasionally medication will block the nerves responsible for ejaculation. However, in the majority of cases, the explanation is far from simple since both psychological and physical causes, in a manner not yet fully understood, combine to block the ejaculatory reflex.

Why is it believed that physical factors may play a part in causing retarded ejaculation?

It is generally agreed that psychological factors such as the contribution of past experiences and a person's feelings or attitudes about sex will play a large part in causing many sexual problems. Less well understood is the part played by physical factors, a person's personality and the physiological processes responsible for sexual function.

For example, the sensitivity of the reflex that triggers ejaculation is known to vary from person to person: in some, it is very sensitive and leads to quick ejaculation; in others, it is very slow and leads to difficulties with ejaculation. It is very unlikely that this variation can be explained entirely in psychological terms, partly because the differences are so great between the quick and slow ejaculators, but also because these two types of responses appear to be associated with other personality characteristics believed to be strongly inherited. Without holding these characteristics at least partly responsible, how else can we explain the fact that, when apparently equally under stress or worried about sex and relationships, some men react by losing their erections, others ejaculate too quickly and yet others find they have difficulty ejaculating?

What kind of psychological factors might make ejaculation and orgasm difficult for a man?
A man who finds it difficult to ejaculate will often have quite rigid views about sex and relationships. He is likely to be quite a 'moral' person, but also one for whom sex is important. Above all, and because he may be particularly self-disciplined, he may find it difficult to lose control of himself and his actions.

Some psychoanalysts believe that men who find it difficult to ejaculate in a woman's vagina are this way because they do not want to 'soil' a woman with their semen. This explanation may sound a bit fanciful, but there may be some truth in it, particularly since it is often observed that men who experience delayed ejaculation with their wives or regular partners do occasionally ejaculate more readily within a relationship that is more casual. The importance of psychological factors becomes very apparent when some men with delayed ejaculation talk about the feelings they have when they approach orgasm during intercourse – they recall that they often seem to be consciously stopping themselves ejaculating in the vagina even though they are not sure why they do this.

What kind of injuries might affect ejaculation?
Any accident (or surgery) that results in an injury to the base of the spine can damage the nerves which serve the reproductive organs and trigger ejaculation. Once these are destroyed, very little can be done to restore their function.

Are there any diseases that might delay ejaculation?
Most of the diseases that are likely to delay ejaculation will also affect erection (see pp. 33–6). There are probably no specific illnesses that bring about a delay in ejaculation alone.

Do men who have difficulty with ejaculation ever have wet dreams?
Although there is no hard evidence to support this suggestion, it is very likely that men who have difficulty ejaculating will be less likely to have wet dreams. If they do have them, this probably shows that their failure to ejaculate when awake has a 'psychological' explanation.

What feelings do women have about their partners who cannot ejaculate when they make love?
On the face of it, it might be expected that at least some women would be quite pleased that their partners do not ejaculate quickly because, as a consequence, intercourse may last longer, thus increasing the chance of her achieving a climax. However, if her partner is never able to ejaculate inside her, her feelings may be more confused. She may feel that it is her fault and even feel rejected as a result. Just as a woman's orgasm may be very important for a man, so his may be important for her, if only as a symbolic expression of his love and need for her. Of course, this problem becomes even more acute if she is trying to get pregnant and ejaculation is rare or absent altogether. Some women will, of course, be upset because they want their partner to ejaculate and get it over with.

Is it true that some men do not ejaculate during intercourse because the walls of the vagina do not provide as much stimulation to the penis as the hand does during masturbation?
Just as the penis, however well designed, is not always the most effective way of giving a woman an orgasm (see Chapter 5), so the vagina is not always the best way to stimulate a man to climax. The penis of a man who takes a long time to ejaculate may need a lot of fairly vigorous and prolonged stimulation, and a moist, dilated vagina in an aroused woman may not be able to provide enough of this kind of intense stimulation.

Also, if a man has spent most of his life masturbating to orgasm, he will have got used to his own special type of stimulation and may find the vagina a very poor substitute for his hand.

What is happening if a man feels he gets an orgasm but does not ejaculate?

This is almost certainly *retrograde ejaculation*. What happens is that the semen carrying the sperm passes backwards into the bladder instead of being carried to the outside through the penis. Normally a valve closes off the bladder at orgasm to stop this happening, but sometimes as a result of surgery, an accident, disease or some types of medication, this reflex does not work. The man will still experience an orgasm, but it will be a 'dry run', and he will not feel the pumping action in the penis because there is no semen to pass through to the outside. This problem can sometimes be treated by drugs or surgery, but if unsolved, it does obviously create real difficulties if he and his partner want a child.

Can the fear of getting his partner pregnant be a reason for delaying or stopping ejaculation?

A fear of pregnancy does appear to be one of the many reasons why a man may prevent himself from ejaculating into a woman's vagina. One of the obvious ways of trying to overcome this fear would be to suggest that he uses a condom or that she uses a reliable method of contraception.

Can a man with no previous problems with ejaculation suddenly find it difficult to ejaculate in a new relationship?

Stress, whatever form it takes, may lead some men to stop ejaculating during intercourse. For example, a man who had never experienced any such difficulties with his first wife found that, when he began a new relationship with a much younger woman, orgasm and ejaculation grew more and more difficult until they became impossible. In therapy, it was discovered that he had become anxious that he could not satisfy her need for intercourse every day, and because they had found it difficult to talk to each other about the problem, his body (i.e. his penis) responded in the only way it could and effectively told them both that something was wrong. Once the problem had been brought into the open, they agreed to have intercourse less frequently, and he was able to relax and he began to ejaculate normally.

Can a single bad experience upset the ejaculatory reflex?

There are many case histories reported in which a single distressing experience appears to have been responsible for a block in ejaculation. This is called *traumatic learning*.

Masters and Johnson[14] describe a case in which a husband and wife were disturbed by their children at a point during their love-making when the man was just about to ejaculate. He was so upset by this that he could not climax afterwards until he had had treatment. A similar experience was reported by a young couple who were disturbed by a policeman when they were having intercourse in a parked car. Delayed ejaculation caused by this kind of experience normally responds well to treatment.

What kind of treatment is used to help men who have difficulty ejaculating?

Retarded or delayed ejaculation is not easy to treat, and because it is fairly rare, there are not many reliable reports on success rates for the various types of treatment available. Very little, at present, can be done to change the physical make-up of a man that makes him likely to delay his ejaculation, but if a therapist takes a careful medical history, this may provide valuable clues about a man's psychology. For example, since the role of his partner is so important, any information about the way in which the man sees her – primarily as mother, mistress, daughter, wife or prostitute – may help the therapist to discover some of the causes of the problem. Once these clues have been identified, they can then be shared by the therapist with the couple, and their greater understanding of what is behind the problem may help them both to work towards a more successful sex life.

Put very simply, this is how psychotherapy, or 'talk therapy', works, and it is an essential first step in the treatment of this and most other sexual problems. Sooner or later, however, a more practical approach will be almost certainly required, and this second stage is called *behaviour therapy* (see pp. 53–7).

What kind of behaviour therapy is used to help men who have difficulty ejaculating?

Most men with delayed ejaculation can masturbate themselves to orgasm. It may take them a little longer than is usual – say, 5, 10 or even 20 minutes – but they usually get there in the end. If, however, they have never ejaculated even after self-masturbation, it is very important that, if possible, they try to achieve this before they involve their partner in treatment.

If ejaculation proves to be difficult or even impossible when they attempt to masturbate themselves, this may be caused by one of the following:

- If they can get an orgasm but do not ejaculate, they may have a condition known as *retrograde ejaculation* (see above).
- They may have had an injury to the spine or an operation that has affected the nerve supply to the penis, or they may be taking some medication which hinders ejaculation.
- They may need so much physical stimulation that masturbation by hand may not provide enough arousal, or they may need additional psychological stimulation not available in self-masturbation.

Retrograde ejaculation can sometimes be treated successfully, and an alternative medication that does not prevent orgasm can often be given. Unfortunately, very little can be done to repair damaged nerves. If a lack of adequate physical stimulation is thought to be the problem, a *vibrator* designed for use on the penis – that is, one shaped like an artificial vagina, usually powered by batteries, or better still, a body massager powered from the mains (see p. 92) – may provide enough stimulation to obtain the desired result. Whatever is tried, it is very important that the man perseveres with his attempts to reach a climax by self-masturbation.

Once he finds that he can masturbate to orgasm, he can then be reassured that his body is working normally. He should continue to practise self-masturbation as often as he can with the aim of speeding up ejaculation, so that he can get an orgasm within 3–4 minutes if possible.

Men who find it difficult to masturbate to orgasm or those who may need up to half an hour of vigorous hand stimulation before they 'come', should experiment:

- Try to lose themselves in exciting, erotic fantasies or use sexually arousing pictures or videos.
- Drink a moderate amount of alcohol.
- Cover the penis with KY jelly or a cream when they masturbate.
- Attempt masturbating in as many different positions and situations that they can think of – for example, standing in front of a mirror, lying on the stomach, in the bath under a shower or whatever turns them on.

The next step is for the man to involve his partner. The plan is to practise masturbating so that he can ejaculate with her being present. Each couple will probably want to experiment at this stage to find the best way. One method is for him to start masturbating himself in the dark, perhaps with his partner lying some distance away. Each time she should get a little closer to him until he can actually ejaculate on her body. She might try helping him come by 'talking dirty' or by enacting some of his fantasies.

Once he has been able to masturbate to orgasm with her nearby, she should start to masturbate him to orgasm. This might prove to be quite easy or it may take some time. One way of going about this is for both of them to masturbate him together, using both his and and her hands on the penis. Slowly his hand can then be removed until she can do it by herself.

When this last step has been achieved, they are ready to experiment with intercourse. Either he or she should masturbate him, and at first, he should try to ejaculate just between the lips of the vulva. The next time, he should place the tip of his penis at the entrance to the vagina and masturbate in this position so that he comes just inside her. Each time they do this, he should try to ejaculate deeper and deeper in the vagina.

Another way is for him to masturbate himself almost to the point of orgasm and then quickly penetrate the vagina so that he ejaculates well inside her. To 'come' inside the vagina for the first time, however it is achieved, is often a very significant step for him, and things may get much easier after that.

If a block still remains and ejaculation in the vagina continues to present difficulties, a return to talk therapy may be necessary. Then another attempt can be made to bring any remaining fears and conflicts to the surface.

Another way of trying to bypass these blocks to ejaculation in intercourse is to use methods of *distraction*. Whatever blocks are responsible for a man's inability to ejaculate, be they physical or psychological, there is no doubt that sometimes they can be modified by sexual novelty, spontaneity or, indeed, by any situation that contains an element of the unexpected. This kind of sexual experience is possibly everyone's fantasy, but for a man who is not able to ejaculate, any scenario that will arouse, distract and focus his concentration away from his fear of failure has a chance of success. Obviously in order to succeed, whatever is tried should, as far as possible, be unrehearsed and, up to a point, unpredictable. Here are a few ideas:

- Make love under a shower or in the bath.
- Have sex in the open air or in a car (ensuring some degree of privacy).
- Have intercourse fully clothed and spontaneously.

Sometimes the treatment outlined above does not work. This may be because the ejaculation reflex requires so much stimulation that normal intercourse is just not able to provide this. Alternatively, it may not work because the man has certain special psychological needs that have to be satisfied before he can ejaculate. If he feels, for example, that ejaculating inside a woman is an insult to her and an assault on her femininity, that it is in some way dirty, these feelings will obviously influence his capacity to 'come' inside someone whom he loves and respects.

If the difficulty he experiences in combining sex and love cannot be resolved by psychotherapy, he may need to experiment with other kinds of relationships, particularly with women who he does not hold in high regard. For example, he may learn to ejaculate for the first time by obtaining 'relief' from a masseuse in a massage parlour. Recently, one of us saw a patient in his 50s who had never ejaculated in his life, either after self-masturbation or during intercourse, but he did so on his first visit to a sauna where the masseuse was able to masturbate him to orgasm. Sometimes such unconventional methods work better than all the best professional advice put together. If by experimenting with these sorts of relationships, he can then learn to ejaculate regularly during intercourse, he may finally be able to transfer this success on to a more valued relationship.

Does behaviour therapy work?

Because delayed ejaculation is a relatively rare problem, there is very little information available on success rates following treatment. Masters and Johnson claimed successes in over three quarters of their patients with this problem, but nothing like this level of success has been achieved by other sex therapists. In the United Kingdom, a 'success' rate of 25 per cent is probably a more realistic expectation.

Is there any form of medication that might help with delayed ejaculation?

Medication has been tried in the past, but by and large, it has proved unsuccessful. Therefore at this stage of our knowledge, it does not form part of therapy.

5.
PROBLEMS WITH ORGASM IN WOMEN

Many women fail to achieve orgasm during intercourse, and although for some this does not appear to matter very much, others can become deeply distressed. Worrying about this kind of problem obviously does not help at all: instead, advice should be sought. Sharing worries will help to put them in perspective, and may also provide an incentive to explore some of the treatment programmes available.

Does a woman always know when she has had an orgasm?
If you asked a man whether he always knew whether he had had an orgasm when he masturbated or made love, most men would have no difficulty at all answering the question. For many women, however, the situation is quite different. This is because, for them, climax may not be such a clearcut experience; this is especially true for those who believe they only rarely have a climax or only experience a very 'gentle' one. Sometimes they are genuinely confused about whether they have had an orgasm or not.

For example, some women, when they have masturbated or made love, simply experience nice sexy feelings around the lips of the vulva and on the clitoris, but these are feelings that never really quite reach a climax and they normally just fade away when stimulation stops. Other women might experience quite intense feelings in their clitoris during lovemaking, a feeling that peaks (orgasm) and then disappears quite suddenly. Then, of course, there are those women who enjoy an unmistakable orgasmic experience that engulfs the clitoris, vagina, uterus and all the surrounding areas. However, there is no clear dividing line between these types of experience, and it is therefore sometimes quite difficult for a woman to know for sure whether she has climaxed or not.

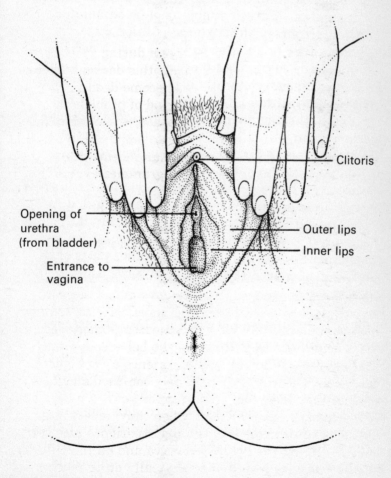

The external view of the vulva

Does the size, shape and position of the clitoris have any influence on a woman's capacity to obtain an orgasm?

The size, shape and position of the *clitoris*, which is a very sensitive part of the vulva, can vary considerably from woman to woman. However, although no proper research has been done, there is no good reason to believe that either the size or the shape of the clitoris has any significant effect on a woman's capacity to achieve orgasm.

Some do complain that their clitoris is in the 'wrong' position so that it does not appear to be stimulated during intercourse. Although the position can vary, it is unlikely that this variation would have a decisive role in helping her to obtain or preventing her having a climax, although naturally it is tempting to assume that a woman with a large clitoris, placed near the entrance to the vagina, is more likely to be orgasmic than a woman with a small clitoris located further away (the average distance between the vaginal opening and the tip of the clitoris is about 2 centimetres). However, the stimulation of the clitoris is often indirect and is achieved by the pulling and stretching of the tissues immediately next to it. Moreover, it is not the only source of arousal for a woman, at least during intercourse; other parts of the vulva and, of course, the vagina can serve as important sources.

Is there a difference between a 'clitoral' orgasm and a 'vaginal' orgasm?

This argument would probably never have surfaced if men had not interfered but instead had left women alone to investigate their own orgasms. Indeed, the whole saga has turned out to be a good example of male chauvinism and, as such, is a story worth telling.

The father of psychoanalysis, Sigmund Freud, started the argument by suggesting that women who could only achieve an orgasm in the area of the clitoris were 'immature' in contrast to those who reported that they experienced a climax both in the vagina and in the uterus. Kinsey[15], the author of the famous *Kinsey Report*, contradicted this. Not only did he attack Freud's 'immature' label as a value judgement without any scientific basis, but he also argued that a vaginal orgasm was a 'biological impossibility' because of the insensitivity of the walls of the vagina. Then Masters and Johnson[16], the American pioneers of sex therapy, entered the fray: they agreed with Kinsey and concluded from their laboratory experiments on volunteer prostitutes that there was only one type of orgasm and this was powered by the clitoris, disposing of the idea of a separate vaginal orgasm as a myth.

Now the argument has gone full circle, and sex researchers (mostly men[17]) have again come round to the view that there are at least two types of orgasm. Not every woman will experience both, and they may blend into each other. There is the orgasm which for want of a better word is called the 'clitoral' orgasm because it is felt mainly in and around the clitoris, and there is a much more deep-seated orgasm felt in the vagina, uterus and surrounding muscles. Gone is the idea that the clitoral orgasm is 'immature' and that the vaginal orgasm is somehow better. Instead, it is now accepted that whichever orgasm a woman experiences depends partly on the type of stimulation she receives (masturbation is more likely to produce a clitoral orgasm), but more specifically, it will be influenced by her personality and physical make-up.

How important are sexual fantasies in helping a woman to reach a climax?

There is little doubt that, if a woman can enjoy good sexual fantasies, particularly when she masturbates, she is more likely to achieve a climax. However, this does not mean that good fantasies automatically make good orgasms since both the capacity to achieve a climax and the ability to fantasize may be linked to a third underlying factor, such as some aspects of brain biochemistry or hormone levels. Therefore, while fantasies and orgasms often go together, there are, of course, many women who enjoy excellent orgasms but who never or only rarely fantasize. Clearly fantasy is not an essential requirement of a woman's arousal in the way that it often is for men.

Sex therapists often try to encourage their women patients with orgasm difficulties to develop their sexual fantasies as a means of achieving a climax. However, some women find this quite impossible, not even knowing where to begin, and the whole process seems quite foreign to them. Should this be the case, and an attempt to teach a woman how to fantasize has failed, it is probably better to concentrate upon other aspects of therapy (described later). Before giving up, however, such women might benefit from reading the excellent collection of fantasies found in Nancy Friday's book *My Secret Garden* (1988)[18].

Can a man always tell when a woman has had an orgasm?

Definitely not! Women's responses at orgasm are so different that it is usually impossible for a man to be sure whether a woman has had an orgasm or not. After all, how can a man tell when sometimes a woman does not always know herself. Obviously, in some cases a woman's behaviour at orgasm is so dramatic, even violent and noisy, that there is no doubt when she reaches her climax. The muscles of her vagina will contract, her cries will become loud and rhythmic, her breathing deeper, often between tightened jaws, her face may go red or white, her whole body will go rigid, then jerk rythmically as the muscles of her body contract and relax with the pulses of her orgasm. Yet other women may make little noise and show few other physical signs of their climaxes. Incidentally, this same kind of variation (though to a lesser extent) is also found in men. Indeed, some women are not even sure,

without investigating, whether their partners have
ejaculated or not.

Is it a good idea for a woman to pretend to have an orgasm in order to please her partner?

This is a very complicated question and not easily
answered. A woman's orgasm is sometimes more
important to her partner than it is for her. If she
guesses that this is so, and if she can act out her
orgasm convincingly, it may possibly be a good idea to
do so, at least from time to time. In practice, this is not
too difficult, since most men are easily fooled and many
women are quite practised at pretending. A woman
may also be tempted to act out an orgasm if she
realizes that her climax would be a signal to her
partner that the end of intercourse is approaching, thus
giving her partner permission to have his climax.

The disadvantage of such duplicity, particularly in a
stable relationship, is that the man, believing his
partner to be satisfied, may not bother to stimulate her
manually and help her to achieve an orgasm during
intercourse, which may be a great loss to them both.
However, perhaps the greatest disadvantage is that, by
adopting this strategy of deceit, she sacrifices the
opportunity to communicate honestly with him and he
with her about their real desires, thereby sabotaging
any chance of understanding the problem, should it
ever become one. Ultimately, each couple must decide
what is right for them, and if they are in doubt, the
best advice is to grasp the nettle and try to talk about
it.

Why do some women have orgasms easily during intercourse yet others find it difficult?

A lot of somewhat inconclusive research[19] has been
done to try to identify some of the reasons for the
differences in the capacity of women to achieve orgasm,
but so far little has come of it.

The main difficulty is that there are so many factors

that could be involved in deciding whether a woman achieves an orgasm easily or not that it is extremely difficult to design a research programme to sort these out. Moreover, a large sample of cooperative women is needed, women who must be able to talk honestly about their sex lives and be prepared to undergo any number of psychological and physiological tests. Because orgasm is not essential for a woman to conceive and reproduce, her climax has not evolved as a biological necessity as it has in the man where ejaculation and orgasm are closely linked, and where as a result problems associated with orgasm and delayed ejaculation are relatively rare. Female orgasm, particularly during intercourse, is a somewhat uncertain event for a large minority – if not a majority – of women, and if sex therapy is to be effective, we need to know much more about the reasons why women differ so much from each other in this respect.

What are the differences between women who find orgasms easy to achieve and those for whom orgasms are elusive or absent?
If you were to make a checklist of those factors that might possibly influence a woman's capacity to be orgasmic, it would probably include the following (though not in order of importance): her general health, both physical and mental; her childhood experiences and relationships with her parents; her personality type (is she extravert or introvert, anxious or placid, assertive or timid?); her attitudes and values about sex; information about her hormones and other relevant physiological data; and the quality of her existing relationship(s).

Until now most investigations[20] have concentrated largely upon the beliefs and attitudes of the women questioned, their relationships with their parents in their formative years and, in particular, their feelings about themselves. Unfortunately, no clear answers have emerged from these investigations, and all that

can be said is that women who find it difficult to
achieve an orgasm often feel anxious, underconfident,
unloved and fearful of rejection. These feelings, it is
said, make it difficult for them to let go and lose
control when making love – a response that is
necessary if one is to achieve orgasm. It was also
observed that many non-orgasmic women had very
poor, distant relationships with their fathers when they
were young. But this is far from the complete story,
and much more exacting research needs to be done
before any clear answers emerge. However, it is likely
that it will be the physiological make-up of a woman
and her personality type rather than her upbringing
that will prove to be important in influencing whether
she is orgasmic during intercourse or not.

Can every woman achieve an orgasm by self-masturbation?

Assuming that, first, there are no medical reasons why
women cannot achieve an orgasm, and second, that
women can give themselves permission to touch and
stimulate themselves adequately, a large number can
learn how to masturbate to orgasm quite easily.
Sometimes a woman may find that she needs the
additional stimulation provided by a *vibrator* – its use
can increase the chances of success quite dramatically.
The main obstacle that a woman has to face in getting
an orgasm by self-stimulation is probably not
physiological but psychological. Many women dislike
intensely the idea of masturbating, but if this
inhibition can be overcome, success is very near.

Is it necessary for a woman to have an orgasm in intercourse in order to get pregnant?

The simple answer to this question is NO. If it were
true, at least one woman in three would find it difficult
to conceive! Sperm travel from the vagina, through the
cervix (neck of the womb) into the uterus and then
along the Fallopian tubes where they meet the ovum at

fertilization. Normally this process takes only a few minutes whether the woman has an orgasm or not. The sperm do not swim but are carried by the muscular movements of the woman's own reproductive system. Because of this, it is thought that a full orgasm may accelerate these contractions, but there is *no* evidence to show that failure to achieve an orgasm makes any significant difference to the chances of successful fertilization and a subsequent pregnancy.

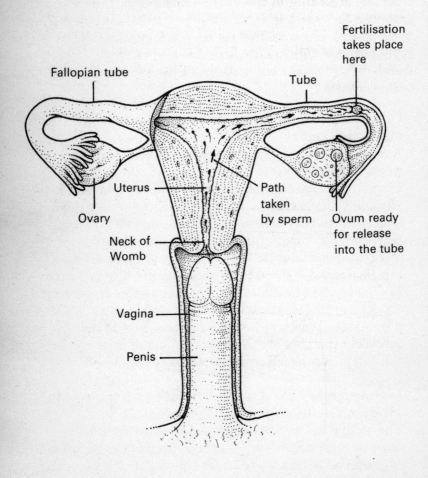

The path taken by the sperm after ejaculation into the vagina

What is a G-spot?

This is said to be a particularly erotic area found inside the vagina – it is named after its discoverer, Ernst Grafenberg a German physician. If a woman lies on her back and puts her finger two or three centimetres or more into her vagina and gently presses upwards towards her pubic hair she may discover her 'G-spot'. Unfortunately, a lot of women do not appear to be able to find it, even when they are sexually aroused. So, whereas, according to the available evidence[21], it probably does exist in some women in others it appears to be absent. If a woman does have a G-spot, stimulation of this area is not only said to be exquisitely pleasant but may also help her to achieve a better orgasm.

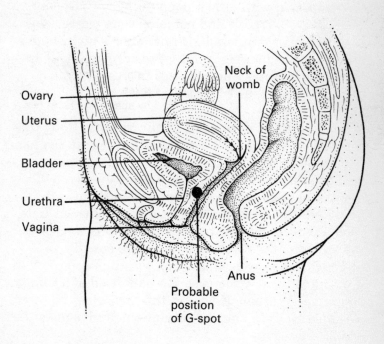

The most likely position of the G-spot

If a woman fails to achieve an orgasm during intercourse, whose responsibility is it – his or hers?

Most men like to feel that their partners can achieve an orgasm during intercourse as a result of the unaided efforts of their penis. This feeling may arise out of a need to please their partners or, perhaps more often, out of a somewhat misplaced arrogance that they can dominate their partners and so arouse them to orgasm. Unfortunately, the reality of the situation is that many women cannot achieve an orgasm during intercourse without some additional manual stimulation and even then this may not be enough. It is therefore quite inappropriate that a man should take on all the responsibility for a woman's orgasm – this is largely her responsibility. Indeed, an over-preoccupation with either 'dominating' or 'pleasing' can be counterproductive and make matters worse. This situation brings to mind Mr Micawber – he lasts five minutes, she climaxes in four – result happiness; he lasts four minutes, she climaxes in five – result, misery. Whose fault? Nobody's fault!

When semen is deposited in the vagina, does this increase a woman's chances of having an orgasm?

Semen contains a substance called *prostaglandin*, as well as sperm. Prostaglandins are involved in a number of bodily functions, and one of them is to stimulate the muscles of the uterus to contract. Indeed, such a process may be involved in helping transport the sperm to the *ovum*. It is therefore possible, although not proven, that when semen is deposited in the vagina, it may increase the likelihood of a woman becoming orgasmic. However, this would not be easily observed since the man's ejaculation often signals the end of intercourse.

Are women who find it difficult to get orgasms during intercourse more likely to be promiscuous?
This sounds like a mischievous question, and there is no reliable evidence to suggest an answer either way. However, good orgasms are a very rewarding experience both for a woman and for her partner, and it is reasonable to suppose that when intercourse regularly leads to her having a good climax, this is more likely to lead to a stable relationship (all other things being equal) than if her orgasms were more elusive or absent altogether. If climaxing is rare, a woman may consciously or unconsciously look for a relationship where there is more physical satisfaction, and this may lead her to experiment with more than one partner.

Does it matter to a man whether his partner has an orgasm?
Sex therapists often report that many men do worry when their partners are unable to achieve an orgasm during intercourse – indeed, sometimes her orgasm is more important to him than it is to her! These men get upset or even angry because they believe that it is their responsibility to give their partners orgasms, and they think that, if they change their technique or postpone their non climax for long enough, they will win in the end. They also worry that, unless their partners achieve orgasm they will become frustrated and look elsewhere for satisfaction – forgetting that there are presumably more valuable reasons for the relationship to survive.

Sooner or later, this performance-oriented view of sex has to be challenged, and the sharing of honest feelings by the partners is the best way of achieving this. For example, if they cannot talk to each other about these things, he may, with the very best of intentions, extend the length of intercourse in the hope that she will get a climax eventually. She then begins to feel soreness and pain in her vagina, which makes it even less likely that she will climax. She may even think that he is finding it difficult to ejaculate, and puts up with the discomfort for his sake, not realizing that he is deliberately delaying his orgasm to help her. The road to hell can so easily be paved with good intentions.

How does a woman feel if she is unable to get an orgasm in intercourse?

We asked a number of women who had difficulty getting a climax in intercourse how they felt about this; not unexpectedly we had a variety of replies. A majority had accepted the fact that orgasms were likely to remain a rare experience for them in intercourse and most were, somewhat reluctantly in some cases, resigned to this. When asked if they would seek help from a sex therapist the answer was generally No. Some of these women thought that it was a bit unfair that men should appear to get so much out of sex, but for a majority the feelings of closeness, warmth, giving pleasure and being needed by their partners was sufficiently rewarding.

On the other hand, there was a minority of women we spoke to who were very upset by their inability to climax in intercourse and quite a few of these women had also found it difficult to talk to their partners about their distress. Some of these women had pretended to climax for years (in order to please their partners) and this often only added to their resentment and anger: some had had brief affairs to see if things were different with other men (usually they were not). Help is available for those who are distressed by their inability to climax, and if nothing else, the sharing of the problem can help to put it in a more sensible perspective.

How does a man masturbate a woman to orgasm?

Both men and women would probably agree that it is easier for a woman to masturbate a man to orgasm than it is for a man to bring a woman to a climax with his hand. Of course, the simplest and most obvious way of solving this difficulty, if it exists, is for her to show him exactly what to do. However, sometimes couples are very shy in bed, and even when they have known each other for years, they often have great difficulty talking to each other about their sexual likes and dislikes.

Naturally, all women will have their own individual preferences as to how they like to be stimulated, but they normally go about it in roughly the same way. In the first place, it is not usual for a woman to put her fingers inside her vagina when she masturbates. Instead, she will probably start by running her fingers between the lips of her vulva until she starts lubricating and begins to feel aroused. She may initially focus her attention on the area just around the entrance to the vagina, but very soon she will usually concentrate most of the stimulation on and around her clitoris. As she becomes more aroused and her clitoris enlarges, it can become very sensitive, even painful to the touch. For this reason, a lot of women masturbate by using a circular motion with two or three fingers *on and around* the clitoris, so as to avoid concentrating too much on the clitoris itself. As a woman approaches orgasm, she may find that it is sufficient for her simply to stimulate the whole of the top of her vulva around the clitoris with the flat of her hand until she finally climaxes.

Ultimately, however, it has to be repeated that there is no substitute for partners' talking to each other or showing each other what to do. In the long run, this approach can only add to the quality of the relationship.

Is a woman more likely to get orgasms at different times in her menstrual cycle?

There is no doubt that the change in the levels of hormones that occurs throughout a woman's menstrual cycle, particularly if she is not on the contraceptive pill, will affect her sex drive and her ability to become aroused. The two occasions when a woman is most likely to feel sexy are at midcycle, when she is ovulating and fertile, and just before and during her period.

Are there any illnesses that would make it more difficult for a woman to have orgasm?

Anyone who feels ill is less likely to feel sexy, so an attack of flu, a backache, headache or stomach-ache will naturally put people off sex. In addition to these common aches and pains, there are a number of diseases that may specifically impair the functioning of either the nerve or blood supply to the vulva, vagina and clitoris, or change the levels of relevant hormones; sometimes a disease will act on brain function. Common diseases that may have such effects are, for example, diabetes, multiple sclerosis, kidney disease, rheumatoid arthritis, sexually transmitted diseases and psychological problems such as depression and anxiety states (see also pp. 33–7).

Why is it easier for a woman to achieve orgasm by masturbation than it is during intercourse?

Just as some men are able to get good erections when they masturbate alone, but fail to become erect when they are with a partner, so many women who find it relatively to easy get an orgasm via self-masturbation will find it difficult or impossible during intercourse. The reasons for this are not difficult to find. Alone, a person can be relaxed, in command of his or her own feelings and fantasies, but with a partner, there are many other factors to take into consideration: concern for his or her needs and hence the need to please ('am I doing it right?'), worries about what the partner might think, and the simple distraction of the 'other person', with all the emotional overtones that any intimate relationship will have. Added to all this is the fact that many women complain that the kind of physical stimulation they receive from the penis is not adequate for them to have an orgasm, whereas in self-masturbation they can 'arrange things differently', give their fantasies free range and even use a vibrator – penises, unfortunately, do not have batteries!

Is there any medication that a woman might be prescribed that may make it difficult for her to get an orgasm?

Most medication, for whatever purpose it is prescribed, will naturally alter body and brain chemistry. Normally these changes do not have much, if any, effect on an individual's sex life except, occasionally, when the consequences may be quite marked. It would be impossible to list here all the drugs that can interfere with sexual enjoyment and, in particular, make orgasm difficult for a woman. Instead we shall only single out the tranquillizers and anti-depressants as particularly serious offenders.

The irony of this is that many patients who seek help because of sexual problems are still prescribed tranquillizers and anti-depressants by their doctors, which often only succeed in making them worse and not better. For example, it has been shown that the tranquillizer *diazepam* (trade name = Valium) may seriously impair a woman's capacity to achieve a climax, as do some of the commonly used anti-depressants, particularly those known as the monoamine oxidase inhibitors (MAOIs). Women who have been prescribed any medicines, the oral contraceptive pill for example, and who find that there is also a marked change in their sexual responses should ask their doctors for their advice.

For what kinds of problems with orgasm do women seek help?

Put very simply, women fall roughly into four broad categories: those who achieve a satisfactory orgasm fairly frequently during love-making and intercourse and who may also, if and when they wish, achieve a climax in self- or partner-masturbation; those who rarely achieve an orgasm during either intercourse or masturbation but are not particularly upset by this; and those who are distressed (and may seek help) because, although they become very aroused during intercourse, they do not normally achieve an orgasm. These latter may also find self- or partner-masturbation unacceptable or unrewarding.

In addition, couples will sometimes seek help because, although the woman may not be particularly bothered by her lack of orgasm, her partner is worried or she is upset because he is upset. Occasionally a woman who has enjoyed good orgasms for many years will find that either gradually or perhaps quite suddenly they are difficult to obtain. There is usually a good reason for this, but without therapy, the couple themselves may find it difficult to understand why it should have happened. Finally, there are those women who have enjoyed climaxes during intercourse in an earlier relationship but find orgasm elusive with their present partner.

What kind of treatment is available to help a woman become orgasmic?

A woman may never have experienced an orgasm by any means at all; she may get a climax via self-masturbation but not during intercourse; or she may have orgasms during intercourse but very, very infrequently. Women may not be at all distressed by any of these situations, enjoying their sex lives and having good relationships. On the other hand, others may become very distressed and consequently seek help.

It should be stressed that self-help is not easy, but even a brief consultation with a sex therapist can make all the difference. This is because the therapist can help to put her problem in its proper perspective – after all, each woman will be different and come for help with a unique set of circumstances. Obviously, many women who seek help are not going to be able to achieve regular orgasms during intercourse however well they follow the advice given, yet others will find that there is marked improvement in the quality of their sex lives. So treatment is certainly worth trying.

The chosen form of psychological treatment for *orgasmic dysfunction*, as it is sometimes known, is once again *behaviour therapy* (see pp. 53–7). This largely practical programme (outlined below) can be done at home. However, before it is undertaken, it is important that the couple, if possible, talk to the therapist together about the 'problem'. Very few women are likely to become orgasmic during intercourse if they have a bad relationship, and they and their partners should try to sort out any conflicts within the relationship to start with, before they tackle the specific issue of 'orgasmic dysfunction'. Finally, it ought to be stressed that probably a majority of sexually active women do find it difficult to achieve climax during intercourse, and some of these may prefer to accept the situation and not regard themselves as having a 'problem' that demands 'treatment'.

What form does the treatment programme take?
The first step is to help the woman understand that she is largely responsible for her orgasm. If she is finding it difficult to get a climax during intercourse, for example, there is no point in her blaming her partner. After all, it is her body and her brain that is responding to him, and unless he is a miracle man, he cannot be expected to take all the responsibility for her problems and inhibitions as well as deal with his own. Of course, he has an important part to play, but many of the changes needed must come from her.

It is necessary for her to try to learn how to masturbate herself. Some women find the idea of touching themselves 'down there' unacceptable – even repulsive – but it is common sense to try to start in this way. To make it easier, she should try to remember that her vulva and clitoris are parts of *her* body and do belong to her. (Her body does not end at her naval!) She should also remind herself that well over half of all women masturbate and, like them, masturbation could also provide her with an important source of pleasure and release from sexual and emotional frustration. Above all, by masturbating on her own, she is much more likely to become aroused and eventually climax, since she will be without any of the distractions that would normally be present when she is making love with her partner.

A woman masturbating herself

It is important that she should arrange to have some 'private time', where she can be by herself when there is little or no risk of her being disturbed. This may not be easy, but it is helpful if she can feel sure that neither the telephone nor the children nor the dog nor door-to-door salespeople will interrupt. The bedroom is a good place to find privacy and security. She should lie down, perhaps put on some music, read a magazine, even pour herself a small drink. She should try to set aside at least half an hour twice a week and not make any excuses to put it off.

There are no rules about how she should start. One way is to explore the kinds of feelings that she might get by touching her breasts, thighs and abdomen. She could use some talc, baby oil or body lotion in this self-massage to see where she gets the nicest feelings.

Sooner or later she will need to touch her vulva. This part of her body may be a mystery to her, and at some point, she should get a hand mirror and place it between her legs so that she can see herself. She may be embarrassed to start with, but she should try to allow her curiosity to overcome her shyness. After all, it is *her* body and the vulva a very important part of it.

The vulva, which is not a widely used term (unlike the word 'penis'), is the name given to the woman's external sex organs. It is made up of two sets of lips (or labia): the outer lips that are covered in hair and are easily visible, and the inner lips that are normally concealed by the outer pair, except when a woman is sexually aroused. These inner lips are very sensitive to the touch, and many women start masturbating by very gently running their fingers between them.

At the top of her vulva inside the labia, she will find her clitoris. Like the penis, it has a very sensitive tip (the glans) and a longer body (the shaft) that is covered by a thin layer of skin. As she becomes aroused, the shaft becomes fatter and harder just like the penis. A little below the clitoris, she will find the entrance to her vagina, and if she feels like it, she might try placing a finger inside.

When a woman becomes sexually aroused, the vagina usually secretes large quantities of a clear liquid. This lubrication will pass to the exterior, moistening the vulva and clitoris. However, some women produce only a little lubrication, and the vulva may remain dry. If this happens, a little baby oil or KY jelly (available at most chemists) placed on the hand or between the labia will help a lot.

As she begins to explore her vulva, she might try to find those parts where touching gives her the most pleasure. She will probably find that it is the clitoris that is the most rewarding place to stimulate. The tip may become over-sensitive, but the shaft can be rubbed quite vigorously: it is here that nerve endings transmit signals to the brain, which will eventually lead her to climax.

Some women like to place one or more fingers inside the vagina when they masturbate, but this is not usual and certainly not necessary to get an orgasm. However, it is a good idea to try everything to see what gives the greatest pleasure.

She must not expect miracles, particularly if she has never masturbated before. It is important to be physically and mentally relaxed, and then, if possible, she should let her mind wander so that she can begin to fantasize. Her fantasies can be romantic or sexual – the idea is to let the mind freewheel and seek out those thoughts that are the most pleasurable, wherever her dreams take her. On this first occasion, she may only experience the mildest of sexy feelings in her vulva and clitoris, and if she gets more than that, it is a bonus. However, it is not unknown for a woman to get a full orgasm the very first time she masturbates. If she finds that she cannot fantasize because other distracting thoughts repeatedly intrude, she should try to let these pass through her mind and then return to her erotic fantasies.

After experimenting for a little while and discovering how to get the best feelings, she may notice that the intensity of the sensations become stronger, her breathing heavier and, as the level of her sexual arousal increases, the erotic sensations spread beyond the vulva into her vagina and uterus. Some women may become frightened of these feelings and stop stimulating themselves. This is because, as they become aroused, they are frightened of losing control. It is very important for a woman to stay with the feelings if she can – otherwise they will simply fade away.

Orgasms may come very quickly or may take a long time to arrive. They may be unmistakable, earth-moving experiences involving the whole of the lower part of the body or just a ripple of pleasure in the clitoris. However, if progress is slow, it is important for a woman to persevere and try to enjoy these private moments with herself even if there are no dramatic results to start with. The importance of fantasy cannot be stressed too much. Some women do find it very difficult to create erotic fantasies for themselves, and if this is so, they should search around for any pleasing thoughts even though they may not be particularly sexual in content – for example, memories of their last holiday or of an enjoyable evening out with friends. However, there are few women who do not have romantic daydreams of one sort or another, and these can lead on to the beginnings of sexual fantasy.

Apart from the fear of losing control as an orgasm approaches, some women stop or allow the feelings to fade away because they feel dirty and sickened by the idea of stimulating themselves in this way. They feel guilty about touching themselves and masturbating just as some men do. This is understandable, but it does help if they can understand that a majority of women do masturbate, that it is not a perversion but instead a valuable alternative to intercourse, and indeed, for some women, it is the only way they are likely to achieve an orgasm. Or, on the other hand, it may help if they remind themselves that the instructions here are primarily aimed at helping them to have climaxes during love-making with their partners so that, if this does become possible, they will then be able to share their orgasms with their husbands or lovers.

If, after three or four weeks of practice, a woman still finds it difficult to experience any kind of climax, she may want to try a vibrator. There are two main types: the battery-operated, plastic penis-shaped ones and the heavier 'body-massagers' that run off the mains. Some women prefer the former because it is a little more manageable, but the batteries do need changing regularly if good vibrations are to be maintained. A good mains vibrator would be similar to the one illustrated below.

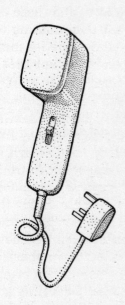

Two types of vibrator

Many women will shy away from the idea of using an artificial aid such as a vibrator. However, thousands are sold every year for this purpose alone, and in many cases, their use can make all the difference between success and failure. A women might even discover by accident or design that a close friend or relative has a vibrator, and can then use this discovery as an opportunity to talk about her feelings.

If the ideas outlined above are followed, most women will be able to experience an orgasm by self-masturbation – indeed, this is one of the few instances in sex therapy where therapists can be reasonably sure of success.

How can a woman who can masturbate to orgasm teach herself how to experience a climax during intercourse?

To start with, it is important that the couple talk to each other openly and honestly about their sexual needs and fears. Most people are vulnerable when they make love, and these doubts and anxieties sometimes prevent them talking to each other. Sharing personal fears and anxieties may not be the whole answer, but it is an important first stage.

A good way to start is for her to masturbate to orgasm in front of her partner. This may not be easy – at first, she may need to do it in the dark or with him some distance away from her. However, if she can, it will help her to learn how to let go without embarrassment in front of him, which of course is a very important step forward.

They might follow this by masturbating together, with both her hand and his hand providing the stimulation in whichever way they enjoy. Then, if possible, the emphasis might be changed gradually so that he alone can bring her to climax. This again is a rehearsal for letting go while still being intimate.

What follows now is simply a series of experiments that each couple must work out for themselves, with the aim of gradually substituting the penis for the hands. In many instances, the transfer from 'orgasm by masturbation' to 'orgasm by intercourse' will not be possible, and many women will still need what is known as 'clitoral assistance', in which where either the man or the woman stimulates the clitoris by hand before, during and after intercourse. One easy way of doing this during intercourse is for the man to enter the vagina from behind. This leaves the clitoris exposed so that either he or she can stimulate it by hand. Alternatively, she can masturbate herself while they are making love in a more conventional position.

One recent survey[22] has shown that as many as 60 per cent of wives and 80 per cent of unmarried women claim that they have never had an unassisted orgasm; some additional form of stimulation during love-making and intercourse was essential if they were to climax. Even if these figures are an over-estimate, they should be remembered just in case a woman ever feels that she is the only one who finds it difficult to get an orgasm during intercourse.

Do these techniques work?

There is little doubt that, if women really want to learn how to get an orgasm via self-masturbation, they (with a few exceptions) should be able to do so. To transfer this experience into intercourse is not so easy, and much will depend upon a woman's personality and physical make-up, and whether she has an opportunity to grow and discover her sexuality either within a stable and supportive relationship or in a series of relationships.

There is much to be said for the view that, since so many women fail to achieve orgasms during intercourse without some additional stimulation, the absence of orgasm cannot really be regarded as a disorder since it is more 'normal' for a woman not to have an orgasm than to have one. The best therapy would then become one of acceptance and understanding rather than a search for the impossible. Finally, it must never be forgotten that, if a woman really does want to reach an orgasm during intercourse, the kind of relationship she has with her partner is very important. These qualities cannot be defined because every relationship is different – perhaps all that can be said is the relationship should be meaningful to her at the time they are making love (or having sex). If it is not and being orgasmic in intercourse is very important to her then she should seek another relationship.

6.
VAGINISMUS

If women find intercourse very painful, sometimes so painful that penetration is impossible, help should be sought immediately. If the diagnosis proves to be vaginismus, there is no doubt that a majority of women can be helped sufficiently to allow them to enjoy normal intercourse, free of any discomfort.

What is vaginismus?
Vaginismus is used to describe a very distressing condition found in women, in which the muscles surrounding the entrance to the vagina contract so tightly that intercourse either becomes impossible or is very painful. These muscular spasms, which usually stop the penis entering the vagina, are quite involuntary and, by preventing intercourse, are the cause of many unconsummated marriages.

How common is it?
Nobody can be sure for certain because many mild cases get better by themselves and go unreported. This is particularly true in young girls just beginning their sex lives, who may experience some temporary discomfort but which is not severe enough to require treatment. It is estimated that about one woman in 100 probably experiences vaginismus badly enough to justify treatment. However, of these women who seek help at sex problem clinics, at least one in every ten

have vaginismus[23]. No woman should ever be discouraged from going for help because she thinks her problem is a very rare condition and the clinic will not know how to help her.

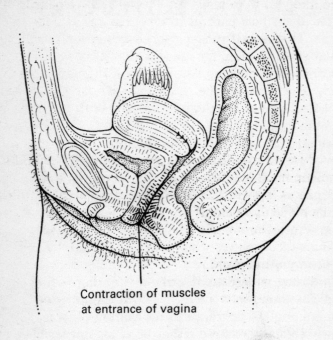

Contraction of muscles
at entrance of vagina

The muscular wall of the lower third of the vagina which on contraction prevents intercourse in women with severe vaginismus

What are the causes?
Nobody is certain what causes vaginismus. However, there is a very strong suspicion that damaging sexual experiences – such as sexual molestation or rape – during childhood or adolescence may trigger vaginismus in a woman when she starts her sex life. However, there are also many women with vaginismus who cannot recall any similar experiences, so clearly this is not the whole story.

Sometimes vaginismus may be caused simply by a heightened awareness of pain. If some discomfort is experienced at first intercourse, which is not an unusual experience, this pain may soon become magnified by the fear of further pain, and eventually this may lead to vaginismus. This cycle of events is more likely to take place in those who have heard stories about how painful intercourse and childbirth can be. The best (if rather poor) explanation available is that some women, for reasons that have yet to be identified, will develop vaginismus if they are under stress. The cause of this 'sex stress' cannot always be identified, and of course, it may have been forgotten by the woman herself.

Is there a particular type of woman who is likely to suffer from vaginismus?

As far as is known, the answer is NO. In other words, it is very difficult to make a firm prediction, based on a girl's personality, whether she is likely to develop vaginismus. However, the 'clinical impressions' of some sex therapists suggest that vaginismus sufferers are often strong-willed and assertive women, but this suggestion has never been properly researched.

What is dyspareunia?

The word *dyspareunia* simply means 'painful intercourse'. This pain can be caused either by *vaginismus, vaginitis* (see below), some other condition (for example, injury to the vagina during childbirth), a very dry vagina or other gynaecological problems. Obviously, when a woman goes to a clinic complaining about painful intercourse, it is very important that a proper diagnosis is made; the course of treatment followed will be different for each condition.

What is vaginitis?

Although the word *vaginitis* literally means 'inflammation of the vagina', in practice it is generally taken to mean 'sore vagina'. Briefly there are two types of vaginitis: first, soreness and pain caused by an infection such as thrush; and second, soreness and pain with a psychological origin, similar to vaginismus. Indeed, it can accompany vaginismus, and like vaginismus, it can be treated by psychotherapy.

Can a woman with vaginismus, for whom intercourse is impossible, enjoy other forms of sexual stimulation?

Yes: with very few exceptions, women who suffer from vaginismus are usually able to masturbate themselves (or ask their partners to) and enjoy good orgasms. Naturally, women with vaginismus would masturbate by stimulating the clitoris and labia (lips) of the vulva and not attempt penetration. Since this is the chosen method of masturbation for many women, those with vaginismus are not particularly disadvantaged in this respect.

Will changing sexual partners help a woman with vaginismus?

Probably not, if the vaginismus is severe and has prevented intercourse for some years. However, many sexual problems are partner-dependent – that is, they disappear or get better in a different relationship. Therefore, occasionally a new partner may provide a way of solving an existing problem, particularly if the vaginismus was the woman's way of telling herself (and her previous partner) that something was wrong with their relationship.

Do women with vaginismus form relationships with a particular type of man?

There is a general feeling, supported by the independent observations of many sex therapists, that women with severe vaginismus tend to choose partners who are less aggressive than average. This is not surprising, bearing in mind that, if the relationship is to survive at all, her partner needs to be kind, considerate and, above all, patient. Although this type

of man may be the one she *wants*, it may not be the
one she *needs*: his tolerance and understanding may
actually serve to perpetuate the symptom because he is
not sufficiently sexually demanding to overcome her
sexual anxieties. On the other hand, some patience and
understanding are obviously called for, and without
help, he may find it difficult to know exactly what to
do for the best. Certainly, he should never force himself
upon his partner because this will simply serve to
increase her anxiety about having intercourse.

How is vaginismus diagnosed? Is the first examination painful?

To find out whether a woman has vaginismus, it is, of
course, necessary for a doctor to examine her. This
examination will not be painful since the doctor will
simply want to know whether or not he or she can
insert a little finger into the vagina. If the vaginal
muscles can be felt closing in on the finger, there will
be no need to go any further.

Is it ever necessary for a woman to have a general anaesthetic in order to establish that she has vaginismus?

Occasionally, in cases of severe vaginismus, it is
impossible to examine a patient vaginally because of
her anxiety: she will simply not allow the doctor to
touch her. In these circumstances, a very brief period
under a light anaesthetic will enable the specialist to
conduct a proper examination and make a correct
diagnosis by eliminating any other causes for her
condition.

How easily is vaginismus cured?

In some case, vaginismus can be cured very easily, in
the space of a few weeks; in other, very severe cases,
therapists report failure, usually when the woman
'drops out' of treatment because there has been no
progress. However, assuming a strong commitment to

complete treatment, the picture is quite an optimistic one. As long as a woman and her partner want to achieve intercourse and believe in the eventual success of the programme, success is very probable.

Masters and Johnson[24] reported no failures in their sample, but other sex therapists claim a success rate of about 50 per cent[25]. The true answer to this question is, therefore, not known for certain, but probably it lies somewhere between these two claims.

Should contraception be used while vaginismus is being treated?

Occasionally, women with vaginismus say that one of the reasons they are frightened of vaginal penetration is because they fear becoming pregnant as a result. Clearly, in these circumstances, the use of an effective method of contraception may help solve the problem. Even if a woman is not frightened of becoming pregnant, it is a good idea to suggest some form of birth control because, otherwise, if the treatment is successful, an early pregnancy may result.

Does a tight hymen ever cause vaginismus?

The hymen, which is a ring of thin skin surrounding the entrance of the vagina, only very, very rarely creates any difficulty at penetration. It is therefore unlikely to cause vaginismus. On the rare occasions that it does, the skin of the hymen is thicker than usual, and this may cause some pain when the penis enters at first, though the hymen is normally stretched quite quickly during intercourse. Therefore, only in a woman who has a very thick hymen and who is also susceptible to vaginismus – a rare combination – would the answer to this question be 'Yes'.

If intercourse is impossible and the woman wants a baby, can artificial insemination be used?

It is possible for a woman with vaginismus to conceive using *artificial insemination* (AI). The semen can be placed on or near the neck of the womb via a long, thin flexible tube (connected to a syringe), which can be easily inserted into the vagina. Should even this insertion prove difficult, artificial insemination can be done under a general anaesthetic, when of course the vaginal muscles will be totally relaxed.

Does having a baby help?

Although it might be expected that a woman who had previously suffered from vaginismus would not experience any problems having once been delivered of a baby, this is not so. If the residual fears and anxieties about the penetration of the penis still persist, the vaginismus will also remain.

Can a woman with vaginismus use tampons?

Generally speaking, women with vaginismus do not use internal tampons because of the discomfort experienced in trying to insert them.

What kinds of treatment are available for vaginismus?

Behaviour therapy is probably the most suitable method of therapy for vaginismus. However, there are other types of therapy available that may prove to be effective for some women. For example, *hypnotherapy* has been reported on occasions to be successful, as has *psychoanalysis*. Surgical treatment of vaginismus, however, should be avoided at all costs – it is never appropriate for this kind of problem.

How is vaginismus treated?

While the following provides a brief account of one approach to the treatment of vaginismus, women seeking help for this condition are strongly advised to obtain professional advice. This is because the supervision and intervention of a therapist can make all the difference between success and failure. Different therapists will use slightly different approaches, but most will follow the scheme set out below, which is based on behaviour therapy. Vaginismus is a *psychosomatic* condition, and so treatment needs to focus on both the mind and the body. The aim of treatment is to help the woman with vaginismus not only to experience intercourse without pain or discomfort but also to enable her to enjoy good sexual feelings at the same time.

Having confirmed, that the woman is suffering from vaginismus, the first thing the therapist will do is to take a full medical history so that he or she can identify the causes of the problem. Such a history is also useful to the woman because it will help her to see the problem in a more objective manner.

Throughout treatment, the woman (and her partner) will continue to keep regular appointments with the therapist – say, once every two or three weeks. During this time, apart from monitoring her past progress and explaining the next stage, the therapist will spend a lot of time listening to her talk about her sexual feelings. At the risk of repetition, it needs to be emphasized that the treatment of all sexual problems requires the commitment and cooperation of both partners. Therefore, an important part of therapy is to help the couple achieve as great a degree of closeness and understanding of each other's needs as possible.

Treatment starts with a 'self-help' first stage, when she is on her own and without the participation of the woman's partner. The idea behind this is for her to try to become happy and familiar with her body and, in particular, with her vulva. She might use a mirror to help her find out exactly where her clitoris is and especially where the entrance to her vagina is, between the lips of the vulva.

The next step is a practical one: when she is free of any risk of interruption and can relax on her own, she should try and explore the area around the entrance to the vagina with her little finger, using a lubricant such as KY jelly. She should be warm, comfortable and perhaps arrange to have some music in the background. She might wish to browse through a magazine or have a drink to relax herself – and, if she can, she should allow herself some sexual fantasies.

At first, she may find it a little difficult to put her finger in her vagina because of the tense muscles surrounding the entrance and because she fears it will hurt, but she must persevere and practise this exercise every day if possible. It may help if she tries to breathe slowly and deeply in and out as she attempts this exercise, since this will help her relax. In addition, she should try to contract and relax the muscles that support this part of her body. For example, if she tries alternatively to relax and contract the muscles that control her bladder (as if she were stopping and starting the flow of urine), this will help to put her in touch with the area around her vagina and enable her to relax.

When she can insert one little finger into the vagina without pain and feels happy about this, she should try two fingers. Some women prefer to use, instead of their fingers, a glass or plastic *dilator* to help achieve penetration (see illustration). These are graded in size from small to large, and can be used in the same way as the fingers. If they are liberally covered with KY jelly, they slip into the vagina very easily. The therapist will be able to provide a set.

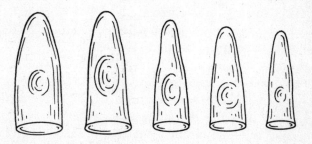

A graded series of vaginal dilators used in the treatment of vaginismus

Sooner or later, the woman will be confident enough to ask her partner to play this part. When they are both sexually aroused, and she feels that she is ready to attempt intercourse, he should lie on his back with his erect penis (covered with KY jelly) pointing upwards. She should gently lower herself on him. She should guide his penis towards the entrance of the vagina. It is very important that she remains in control and that, at this stage, he takes no initiative and makes little movement.

Gradually deeper and deeper penetration can be tried until his penis is fully inserted. Then, and only then, can he begin to become a little more active and thrust very gently. Once penetration in this position, has been achieved other positions of intercourse can be tried.

From time to time, the tightening of the vaginal muscles and the accompanying pain may return. If this does happen, the couple should make a decision to carry on, proceeding very gently in the early stages of penetration. This is important because many couples find excuses for not continuing treatment, and there may be long intervals without any attempts at penetration. If possible, no more than three to four days should pass without returning to the programme.

Can vaginismus and dyspareunia ever be cured by other means – that is, without having to use the practical approach described above?
Yes: sometimes the symptoms of pain and discomfort experienced during intercourse are largely a woman's reponse to the poor relationship with her partner. Where this appears to be one of the main reasons for the vaginismus or dyspareunia, therapy that focuses on restoring good communication and understanding between the couple can lead to a disappearance of the symptoms. This type of 'talk therapy' is, of course, an essential part of the treatment of vaginismus and dyspareunia anyway, and is particularly important if there are early childhood experiences that may have contributed to the problem and need to be brought out into the open.

7.
HOMOSEXUAL AND LESBIAN BEHAVIOUR

Those who are homosexual, lesbian or bisexual do not have a sexual problem as such, except that they live in a predominantly heterosexual world with its inevitable prejudices. In the short term, this situation cannot easily be changed, but support, advice and a listening ear can make all the difference between what may be, for some, a miserable existence and an acceptance of and pride in the fact that they are gay.

What is a homosexual?
A homosexual is someone who is sexually and/or emotionally attracted to a member of their own sex. Both men and women can be homosexuals. The word 'lesbian' is used to describe a female homosexual, while the description 'gay' usually refers to a male homosexual. There is no hard-and-fast-distinction between homosexuals and heterosexuals because many gay people also have heterosexual relationships; they may even be married and have children. For this reason, it is wrong to use the word 'homosexuality' as if it were something quite distinct from 'heterosexuality'.

Men and women who can enjoy sex with their own and with the opposite sex are called 'bisexuals'. They usually have a preference for either men or women, but sometimes the attraction is evenly balanced.

How many people enjoy homosexual sex?

About 5 per cent of all adult men – that is, one man in 20 – will have had quite a lot of homosexual experience during their lives. Half of these men – about one in 40 – will be exclusively homosexual and will never have been sexually attracted to women. In addition, there are a large number of men, perhaps as many as one in three, who will have had some homosexual experience, although this may have occurred only on very rare occasions or perhaps only once or twice[26].

It seems that far fewer women are lesbians. Surveys[27], if they are to be relied upon, suggest that about one women in 50 (2 per cent) prefer sex with another woman. However, this is probably an underestimate. The number of women who enjoy sex with other women is likely to increase as all women begin to take charge of their own lives and do what they really want to do with their minds and bodies.

The percentages of people who are gay seem very small at first sight, but if they are correct, this means that well over a million people in the UK alone enjoy gay sex from time to time.

How can a person tell whether they are gay or not?

If a person occasionally finds him/herself attracted to a member of the same sex, this certainly does not mean that person is going to be homosexual all his or her life. Many young people have crushes on older men and women of the same sex as themselves, and a very large number of children and adolescents of the same sex experiment and play very intimate sex games together[28].

Most of these youngsters will eventually find that they prefer the opposite sex. However a few, either because they are very shy and find same-sex relationships less threatening, or because, deep down, they know intuitively that the opposite sex holds no promise of any physical or emotional attraction, will discover that gay sex is going to become an important part of their lives.

It is not easy to know for sure, particularly when we are young, whether we are really gay, bisexual or just going through a short-lived stage of needing gay experiences. One clue that may provide some help is to use the context of the sexual fantasies used in self-masturbation as a guide. If the nature of these fantasies is largely homosexual, it is very probable that gay needs are quite strong. On the other hand, if the fantasies are very mixed – homosexual, heterosexual and bisexual – this would suggest some uncertainty about our sexual needs and that the gay interest may only be temporary. Many homosexual men and women do not find heterosexual sex unpleasant – in fact, some enjoy it occasionally for a change. Normally, it is the emotional part of the relationship that holds no attraction.

What decides whether a person is homosexual, bisexual or heterosexual?

All sorts of theories and ideas have been proposed, but the simple answer is that we do not know for sure. Some research[29] has suggested that the tendency to become either homosexual or heterosexual is quite strongly inherited, and that therefore homosexual behaviour has a genetic or biological basis. Others have produced evidence[30] that supports the view that whether one is gay or heterosexual will instead depend largely upon the nature of early childhood experiences within the family. Probably the true explanation will prove to be a combination of both these theories.

What is evidence in support of the view that homosexual behaviour is partly inherited?

Those who argue that heredity plays a large part in making a person homosexual quote the results of studies of twins[31]. These have shown that there is a much greater chance of a pair of identical twins (who share the same genes) *both* being gay, rather than *both* of a pair of non-identical twins (who, on average, will only share half their genetic make-up).

These researchers also point out that whether a person becomes gay or not is very important biologically, for the simple reason that gay men and women are less likely to have children; this could be a great disadvantage to the species if homosexual behaviour became too widespread. Therefore, it is argued, the mechanisms (whatever they are) that influence the direction of the sex drive towards the same or opposite sex could not be left to the somewhat unpredictable outcome of early experiences met in childhood, because of the serious consequences to mankind. It would be rather like allowing the chance effects of upbringing to determine the equally important decision of whether a pregnancy was going to result in a male or a female baby.

No one is suggesting that homosexuals differ from heterosexuals in their sex chromosomes. However, those who support the hereditary explanation of gay sexual preference would claim that there are a number of subtle biological differences between homosexuals and heterosexuals that have yet to be identified.

Is there any scientific evidence that homosexual behaviour is caused by upbringing?

The evidence[32] in support of the theory that gay behaviour results from particular kinds of parent–child relationships is somewhat contradictory and not very convincing, even though upbringing may well tip in favour of one sort of sexual preference or another. Obviously most gay men and women are brought up as heterosexuals, so it is unlikely that they could have simply learned to be gay at a young enough age for this to have had an effect upon them. However, it has been suggested that a man who had a poor relationship with his father, either because he was absent from the home for long periods or because he was unloving and impersonal, is more likely to become gay. If, as might happen in those circumstances, his mother was also over-protective, seductive and 'smothering', this experience might also add to the likelihood of him growing into a homosexual.

More recent and exacting research[33] has, however, thrown some doubt upon this conclusion: when the life histories of well-adjusted homosexuals and heterosexuals were compared, no significant differences in their upbringing were discovered. Other research[34] which appears to confirm the importance of upbringing has shown that, when the family backgrounds of lesbian girls was examined, one of the reasons for their gay behaviour was that they appeared to have received insufficient love from their mothers. This, combined with poor relationships with their fathers, led them to seek out love from other women.

However, good research of this kind is very difficult and expensive to undertake, and the results obtained are not always particularly reliable and are often capable of several different interpretations. Perhaps the only general conclusion possible is that there is nowadays a trend away from believing that upbringing is a 'cause' of homosexual behaviour and a result of 'improper parenting'.

If upbringing is recognized by some as being important in making a man gay, how does having an 'over-protective mother' and a 'distant' father play a part?
To form satisfactory relationships with members of the opposite sex, it is necessary for the adolescent boy to separate himself from his parents and transfer his feelings to a girl of roughly the same age. If, for example, a boy has a very close relationship with his mother, he may find this separation difficult, and although he may achieve it physically (that is, leave home), he may find the separation more difficult psychologically. In other words, his first 'love affair' with his mother has coloured his feelings towards all women. This is called the *Oedipus complex*. No one has

yet proved that homosexuals are more likely to develop
an Oedipus complex than heterosexuals, but this has
not prevented those who argue that upbringing is
important in triggering homosexual behaviour from
believing that the incestuous feelings that some men
feel towards their mothers outlaw all other women as
prospective partners, with the result that only men are
left to relate to emotionally and sexually.

The absence of a good relationship with his father is
also said to complicate a growing boy's feelings towards
other males. He may regard men differently, simply
because he was never able to relate to his own father
properly, stand up to him when they had rows and
eventually take over his role as a heterosexual male.

Is homosexual behaviour an illness?

It is very difficult to defend the view that it is an
illness. Homosexuals are often very happy, adjusted
men and women. They will, of course, have problems –
living in a largely heterosexual society is one of them –
but so do heterosexuals. The idea that 'homosexuality'
is a disease is simply society's way of disapproving of a
minority that it still often regards as unacceptable.

Why is there so much prejudice against homosexuals?

Most people are prejudiced against minorities. Racial
groups are an obvious target, but added to this could be
those who are mentally ill or handicapped and those
who are physically handicapped or deformed. Martyrs
and witches have been burned at the stake often only
because they were regarded as being in some way
different, and homosexuals have been pilloried and
persecuted throughout history in many cultures for the
same reason. Even today, both the Church of England
and the Roman Catholic Church (among others) seek to
preserve these prejudices by emphasizing the
'sinfulness' of homosexual behaviour, as did the British
government under Margaret Thatcher through

legislation resulting in the infamous Section 28 of the Local Government Act, 1988, which prevents local councils from doing anything that 'promotes' homosexual behaviour (be it funding a play dealing with homosexuality or buying library books with a homosexual theme).

These cultural pressures against homosexuality can be very powerful and take many forms. For example, when gay men are described as 'poofs', 'queers', 'fairies' or 'fags', the implied insult serves to ridicule and hopefully suppress their behaviour.

The real reason for the existence of these prejudices is that all established social groups feel the need to purge themselves of outsiders to preserve their own identities. Such a reaction also helps to provide each society with easily defined guidelines as to what is acceptable behaviour and what is not. However, it is to be hoped that changes will begin to take place in modern societies, changes that will increasingly allow their members more freedom to find themselves, so that the role of prejudice as a regulator of behaviour will itself be eroded.

Is homosexual behaviour becoming more widespread?

Most human behaviour is governed by inherited predispositions – a kind of genetic straight-jacket that limits what is possible for any one person. However, despite this biological straight-jacket, there is still some considerable room for manoeuvre, and as social restraints relax and homosexuals can 'come out' and be seen to be gay without too much fear of prosecution, persecution or ridicule, so 'homosexuality' will appear to be on the increase. However, even if the pressures against being gay were removed overnight, it is very unlikely that homosexual behaviour would increase dramatically. For biological reasons – that is, the survival of the species – heterosexual behaviour will, for the foreseeable future, always be more common.

If gay behaviour is at least partly inherited, how do the genes responsible remain in the population if homosexuals do not normally have any or many children?

Unless this question can be answerd satisfactorily, the genetic theory of 'homosexuality' is open to doubt. However, biologists have discovered a number of similar parallels in which inherited characteristics that may be a great handicap to individuals and lead to the failure of reproduction are still found in the species.

For example, schizophrenics, because of their illness, may not be able to have long-term relationships, or if they do, they will almost certainly have fewer children than average. Fibrocystic disease of the pancreas – commonly known as *cystic fibrosis* – is another very common inherited disease in which, because of the severity of the illness, those suffering from it do not often marry and have children. However, in both these instances the numbers of schizophrenics (about 1 per cent of the population) and the incidence of those with cystic fibrosis (about one in 2000) remain unchanged.

To explain this somewhat surprising observation, biologists argue that these genes survive in the population because the brothers and sisters or other close relatives of sufferers of these inherited conditions, with whom they naturally share some of their genes, have more children than average. In this way, they ensure that the genes, which though not fully expressed in these near relatives but simply carried by them, are kept in the population. According to this theory, the same thing would be true of 'gay genes'.

Alternatively, 'gay genes' might survive because gay men and women are more successful than average. It is well known that, nowadays, homosexuals do very well in some professions – the theatre and the media, for instance – and historically, they may also have had certain skills that led them to higher-than-average success. As a result, the increased wealth and status of some homosexuals might have led to a greater chance of survival of their families, who benefited from the support they received from their gay relatives, and this would, in turn, increase the chances of survival of the gay genes they carries. Finally, genes that tip the balance towards a homosexual lifestyle may possibly be preserved in the population by the fact that, although most male gays do not have any children, many (about one in five in one study[35]) lesbians do.

Why do gay men have more sexual partners than heterosexual men?

The average homosexual man will have about ten sexual partners every year while he is sexually active, in contrast to the average heterosexual man who will only have about six partners in a lifetime. However, the little research that has been done into this phenomenon suggests that homosexual men do appear to have a lower sex drive than their heterosexual counterparts. They have less need for sex so, rather than establishing long-term relationships with a few partners (when sex would be available most of the time), the greater number of partners enjoyed by homosexual men probably satisfies their need for sexual variety rather than any need for more sex. Heterosexual men, by and large, have the stabilizing influence of a woman and a family to help them regulate their promiscuous needs, whereas homosexual men do not. Many gay couples do establish long-lasting, monogamous relationships but even these often allow quite a lot of sexual freedom.

This is in contrast to some lesbian relationships where the need for sexual variety is much more limited. All that this seems to suggest is that male homosexuals are more promiscuous simply because men are by nature more promiscuous than women. However, a recent survey of lesbians[36] not in stable relationships, found that gay women had more sex than heterosexual women, more orgasms, a greater number of partners and a higher level of sexual satisfaction.

113

What do homosexuals do to one another when they make love?

Touching, kissing and mutual masturbation are the most frequent ways that young male and female homosexuals begin their sex lives. Oral sex – *cunnilingus* for women, *fellatio* for men – is also very popular. On the other hand, anal intercourse is not practised by gay men as widely as is generally thought – only about one in six regularly make love in this way. Of those that do, the majority say they prefer taking the active role. Lesbians normally arouse each other by mutual stimulation of the clitoris, either by hand or orally; penetration of the vagina either by a finger, dildo (artificial penis) or vibrator is not done very often. Cunnilingus is widely used by lesbians as a means of bringing both partners to orgasm.

It is said that, when homosexual men and women make love, there is much more communication and tenderness between them in sex play than with heterosexuals who, at least in stable relationships, just 'get on with the job'. This difference may, of course, be partly due to the fact that many homosexual relationships are often new, and novelty, excitement and the need for intimacy still remain. It may also be because there is likely to be more empathy and understanding between two people of the same sex when they make love.

Could anyone have gay sex if the circumstances were right?

It is not very difficult to imagine a situation where both men and women who are normally exclusively heterosexual might be tempted to experiment and even enjoy a homosexual encounter. For example, in prison where there is no opportunity for heterosexual sex, homosexual behaviour is very common in both men and women, but when these prisoners are discharged, they return to their often exclusively heterosexual

ways. Clearly to have a gay experience in such
circumstances does not make someone a homosexual.

Do homosexuals have sexual problems like heterosexuals?

Yes, they do, and moreover, they appear to be very
similar to those experienced by heterosexuals. For
example, the most common difficulty for which gay
men seek help are problems with erection. Premature
ejaculation is also quite common but, as is found in
heterosexuals, delayed ejaculation is rare. Gay men
also have problems with their relationships, with low
sex drive and, of course, with sexually transmitted
diseases.

Very little is known about the sexual problems of
gay women, although it would be surprising if they
were very different from those found in heterosexual
women. The only exceptions would be vaginismus,
which would normally not present too much of a
problem to a lesbian, nor, or course, would unwanted
pregnancy!

Are male homosexuals normally effeminate and lesbians 'butch'?

The popular stereotype of the camp, effeminate gay
man and the masculine, butch lesbian is a myth and
does not reflect reality. Of course, there are some gays
who are immediately recognizable as such because of
their appearance, speech and manner, but these are the
exceptions. Indeed, what is really quite surprising is
the fact that 'brain sex' (the way a person thinks) and
'body sex' (the way a person looks) can be so strikingly
different. Heterosexual men may find many gay women
very attractive physically and often find it hard to
believe that they are gay. To a lesser extent,
heterosexual women also find some gay men very
attractive sexually and have even been heard to
complain, 'What a waste!'

Do sex hormones have any part to play in making someone homosexual?

Apart from one or two isolated and unsubstantiated studies[37], there is no convincing evidence that the levels of sex hormones circulating in the blood of gay men and women are any different from those of heterosexuals. However, it is possible that testosterone, the male sex hormone secreted by the testes (but which is also present in women in small amounts), may influence the development of the brain in the unborn foetus. During pregnancy, the male foetus produces testosterone from its minute testes, and the presence of this hormone ensures that the baby will develop a penis and scrotum. (Without testosterone, the child would have a vulva and clitoris.)

There is also quite a lot of evidence, particularly from animal studies, that the same hormone, testosterone, will also modify the development of a part of the brain called the *hypothalamus*, which is responsible, among other things, for regulating sexual behaviour. If these observations are applied to humans, it could be that, if testosterone is present at a critical point in the brain development of the unborn child, it may influence the 'wiring' of the nerve 'circuits' in the hypothalamus so that 'male' behaviour is more likely. In the absence of testosterone – for example in a female foetus, where this hormone is normally absent because there are no testes – the brain circuits would be 'wired' in such a way that 'female' sexual behaviour is more likely. It has been suggested[38], therefore, that homosexual behaviour may be more likely in men who have insufficient testosterone present during this stage in their development, and that, arguably, gay behaviour in women is more likely if they had too much testosterone at this time (the hormone could have passed over the placenta from the mother's circulation).

The influence of hormones as an explanation of some types of gay behaviour has never been very well received by the gay community, nor has it been confirmed scientifically, but it needs to be considered alongside all the other evidence. However, even if the role of prenatal hormones was shown to play a small part in triggering gay behaviour, it would only be one of many factors likely to tip the scales.

Will injections of the 'male' hormone testosterone make gay men heterosexuals?

No. There have never been any reports that, as a result of receiving injections of testosterone, gay men have noticed any differences in their behaviour, apart from perhaps, in some, a very short-lived increase in their sex drive.

Is there any therapy that might help a homosexual to become heterosexual if he or she so wishes?

It is very unlikely indeed that any form of known treatment, physical or psychological, is going to result in changing a man or woman who has been a practising homosexual for some time. The role of therapists in these circumstances is to try to find out why these people are seeking help, establish why they are distressed and then attempt to help them accept that part of themselves that is gay. A common suggestion is a change of lifestyle to one that will reduce stress and anxiety, and of course, therapists can play a very important role in providing support for those who are deeply upset and confused by what appears to them as an insurmountable problem. Indeed, sometimes by simply *accepting* the fact that you are gay results in a great sense of relief.

Therapy can be particularly helpful for young men and women who are seeking advice because they are uncertain about whether they are gay or not. In late adolescence and early adulthood, many young people may be very confused by the fact that some of their sexual fantasies concern individuals of the same sex. They may never have had any sexual experience whatsoever – they feel shy, embarrassed or hostile in the company of the opposite sex, but feel equally guilty about their homosexual fantasies. Simply talking about these conflicts can be very helpful. For example, if a therapist explains to a young man that perhaps his homosexual fantasies are there, not because he is gay, but simply because he feels very underconfident about his ability to cope with girls, a lot of anxiety may be lifted. On the other hand, it may sometimes be necessary for a young person to begin to accept his or her gay nature. Obviously, in this kind of counselling situation, the therapist has to be very skilled and sensitive, and must avoid at all costs imposing his or her feelings on to the young person.

What is aversion therapy?

This is a type of behaviour therapy designed to change people so that an unwanted behaviour can be reduced or eliminated altogether, to be replaced by a more acceptable alternative. The subject is usually shown a video of the unacceptable behaviour and at the same time receives an electric shock (or perhaps is given something really objectionable to smell). Shortly afterwards, the desired alternative behaviour is displayed on the screen but without the punishment.

While aversion therapy was at one time used quite extensively by psychologists and psychiatrists in their attempts to help homosexuals change into heterosexuals, there is no evidence that it was particularly successful in achieving this. Indeed, all it did was to alienate the homosexual community from the medical profession. Sometimes aversion therapy is used in the 'treatment' of sexual offenders such as rapists and paedophiles (see Chapter 8) and with some success, but it clearly has no part to play in modifying homosexual behaviour.

8.
UNUSUAL SEXUAL BEHAVIOUR

Those many men, and fewer women, who enjoy unconventional sex need support and advice as much as anyone. Usually very little can be done to change their behaviour, but understanding and sympathy can go a long way towards improving their lives if they are sufficiently distressed to seek advice.

What is meant by the term 'unusual sex'?
Not so long ago, homosexuals, exhibitionists, transvestites and those into bondage and into voyeurism were all lumped together and labelled 'sexual perverts'. As time has passed and an understanding and tolerance of these behaviours has slowly come about, slightly less harsh and less punitive descriptions were used. Instead, labels such as 'sexually deviant', 'sexual anomaly' and, finally, 'sexual variation' were used to identify those who engaged in sex that was a little out of the ordinary. Strictly speaking, sexual behaviours that are unusual are known as the *paraphilias* (unusual loves), yet even this delightful word has, for example, been defined (and defiled) in the 1983 edition of the *Chambers Twentieth Century Dictionary* as 'sexual perversion' and 'abnormal sexual practices'.

Because 'unusual sex' can take so many forms, it is not easy to define it precisely. Perhaps it is best described as any unconventional or statistically unusual way of behaving sexually that plays an important and regular part in a person's sex life.

What sexual behaviours would normally be regarded as 'unusual'?

There are many ways in which a minority of men and women (although mainly men) depart from straight heterosexual love-making and intercourse. Nowadays neither masturbation nor oral sex, for example, could be described as unusual (though they were previously condemned), and generally speaking, homosexual behaviour between adults is now more or less accepted. There do, however, remain a collection of sexual activities, often given quaint names, that are, statistically speaking, quite rare – in other words, possibly a maximum of only one in 200 men are involved in each. Most of these behaviours (but not quite all) are harmless.

- A *voyeur*, usually a man, gets most of his sexual satisfaction by seeking out opportunities in which he can observe women either in various states of undress or having sex. Sometimes this is known as being a 'peeping Tom'.
- An *exhibitionist* is a man who has a very powerful and often uncontrollable urge to display his penis (erect or otherwise) to unsuspecting women in order to shock them and arouse him.
- A *fetishist* is usually a man who needs the presence of certain objects before he can get turned on sexually. These objects may be, for example, a woman's shoes, her underclothes or even locks of hair.
- *Sadomasochism* includes a wide variety of behaviours, all of which involve either giving or receiving pain in one form or another as part of the process of becoming sexually aroused.
- Those who are into *bondage* require, as the name

suggests, that either they or their partners are tied up or restrained in some way during love-making.

- A *transvestite* is a man who can only enjoy sexual arousal by dressing in a woman's clothes, yet at the same time, he feels emotionally at peace with himself. This is also known as 'cross-dressing'.
- A *paedophile* is a man (and, occasionally, a woman) who is sexually attracted to young children of either sex.

In addition, there are many other types of often quite rare sexual activities that could also be classed as paraphilias. For example, some men need intimate contact with either faeces or urine (known, respectively, as *coprophilia* and *water sports*) or with animals (*bestiality*), or need enemas to become aroused (*klismaphilia*), and so on. The list is endless.

Incest – that is having sex with a member of one's own immediate family – and *rape* (forceful intercourse) are not, strictly speaking, paraphilias, since they are usually (though not always) opportunist activities and not a permanent feature of a man's sexual behaviour. An exception to this, of course, would be instances of prolonged child sexual abuse.

Sometimes these unusual behaviours account almost entirely for a person's sexual outlets, yet in others they may only be enjoyed occasionally simply to enhance what might otherwise be regarded as 'straight' sex. Labels are therefore misleading, since there is no clear distinction between the usual and the unusual.

Why is it that more men than women enjoy unusual sex?

Whatever the future holds for the ever-changing sexual and social roles of men and women, there is little doubt that, at least at present, there are some differences between most men and women in the way they behave socially and sexually. We have no doubt that many of these differences will eventually disappear, when it will become more sensible to talk about the variations between 'people' and not between 'men' and 'women'.

The present differences between the sexes is nowhere better illustrated than in the way in which men and women take to unusual sex: paraphilias are common in men and rare in women. But why should this be so? Most men tend to be predatory when it comes to sex – women tend to be more reserved – and at least in the past, men have competed with each other for what is, after all, a limited resource – sex. For this reason, there will be more losers among men than among women, and very often it is these losers in the sexual and emotional rat race who practise unusual sex. Even if couples do struggle on in one or more monogamous relationships, the need for sexual novelty still lingers on in many men, and this yearning may be expressed in paraphilias.

Biology and society have, in the main, programmed the boy to be sexual and not emotional, whereas the girl is taught to be emotional and not sexual. Therefore, there are going to be some casualties, particularly among the sexually non-competitive boys. Moreover, the boy needs to leave behind the love of his first girlfriend (i.e. his mother) but the girl does not have to escape the attentions of her father to the same extent, if only because the latter is less likely to be as involved in her upbringing as her mother was. And even when the boy is older, there still remains the inescapable biological fact that men have to get erections before they can make love.

For all these reasons, it is not surprising that there are more sexually underconfident and shy men than women, men who have either no opportunities for sex or very few. These so-called *heterophobic* men do need to find outlets for their damaged sex lives and, as a result, seek out these unusual sexual behaviours. Self-masturbation and fantasies are the easiest and most obvious way of having sex without a relationship – hence the implied insult when a man is called a 'wanker'. However, the variety of paraphilias described in this section help to give some idea of the ways in which these vulnerable men may seek satisfaction.

No doubt the scene will change as Victorian attitudes ultimately disappear and as the sex roles become less distinct. Indeed, women might even begin to take a greater interest in unusual sex; prostitution and exhibitionism (e.g. strippers) are the favourites at the moment, but who knows what other ways women might use as a means of expressing their sexuality unconventionally. Perhaps the forerunner of this is the occasional recent appearance of the female obscene phonecaller.

What makes a man or a woman a voyeur?

Many of these so-called 'paraphilias' are to be found in a mild form in everyone. Certainly there is a voyeur lurking in most of us: who doesn't momentarily turn to watch a couple embracing, and how many men could walk away from an opportunity to watch, unobserved, an unknown woman undressing, let alone making love? Indeed, the extent and popularity of the soft and hard porn industry is evidence of a near-universal interest in watching others having sex.

For most, these voyeuristic needs play only a minor part in their lives, yet for others, this desire to observe others in sexually intimate situations becomes compulsive. The voyeur is usually a shy sexually inhibited man, who feels guilty and underconfident about relationships. Because he may have difficulty expressing his sexual and loving feelings to one person, a characteristic of many of those who enjoy one or more of the paraphilias, he will seek out sexual arousal in ways that will provide him with 'relationship-free' sex.

The growth of the video industry has provided at least some voyeurs with a safe and legal way of satisfying their needs. The experience of Denmark[39], where the number of prosecutions against 'peeping Toms' (as well as against the perpetrators of many other sex crimes) fell as a result of the legalization of pornography, is likely to be paralleled in the UK as video-porn becomes increasingly available.

Why should a man want to expose himself and display his penis to a woman he does not know?

Although many women, and not a few men, might regard indecent exposure as offensive, disgusting or even frightening, exhibitionism, more than any other paraphilia, is usually a sign of a profound sexual inadequacy, and those who practise it are unlikely to be a real threat to anybody. Admittedly, the experience can be very embarrassing, but it should be remembered that, if a man is driven to exposing himself in public, it is a fairly good indication that he is unlikely to do much else with his penis.

For most men, a hard, erect penis is very important – nothing provides as much evidence of their manhood – and, of course, many women find the sight of an erect penis arousing, though usually as a part of making love. It is not surprising, therefore, that a sexually underconfident man, with perhaps little opportunity for a sexual relationship, will in desperation want to show himself off in this fashion. This may be his only way of calling attention to himself and obtaining some kind of reaction from a woman, whether it is pleasure, shock, derision or disgust.

From the woman's point of view, the best way to deal with this kind of problem is to ignore it and walk away. From the man's point of view, counselling and behaviour therapy may help, but like many of the other paraphilias, exhibitionism is not easy to treat successfully and sometimes the judicial system has to intervene. Of course, there are many women exhibitionists who enjoy posing and displaying themselves in bikinis or topless or even in the nude. However, presumably because women exhibitionists are not regarded as a threat to anyone, the law does not concern itself with them. Kinsey[40] pointed out this dichotomy when he wrote that, if a man stands at a window naked and is seen by a woman, he is arrested for indecent exposure, but if a woman poses at a window naked and is seen by a man, he is arrested for being a voyeur!

Why do some men need fetish objects to become sexually aroused?

Sex is a very powerful drive that begins to express itself very early on in childhood. This may not be very obvious to parents, and even children themselves may not be fully aware of their sexual fantasies, which can be present long before they reach puberty. By a process called *imprinting*, sometimes objects that are not specifically sexual can take on a very special meaning for children – particularly males – so that, eventually, when they are grown up, they find that they cannot become aroused without them.

To some extent, most men have a perfectly healthy fetishistic interest in women's clothes – high-heeled shoes, bikinis, tight jeans, suspenders, all have a sexual aura of their own. Magnify that a 100 times and perhaps then it might be possible to understand how a clothes fetishist feels. These men may go to great lengths to satisfy their needs, purchasing (through advertisements in newspapers and specialist magazines) women's soiled underwear or stealing it from washing lines. Rubber and leather fetishists (known as 'rubberites' and 'leatherites') have a compulsive need to dress in leather or rubber gear, and have their own magazines, videos and clubs. It is thought that rubber and leather may have sexual associations because of their texture or perhaps because leather, in particular, has certain obvious links with bondage, or perhaps animals.

Like many other paraphilias, the need for fetish objects in a man is usually a sign that he finds it difficult to package his sexual and loving feelings together in one relationship. He uses the fetish objects as a way of ritualizing the sex act to exaggerate the sexiness of his partner at the expense of loving feelings, which may get in the way of his sexual arousal during intercourse.

Women may also have a need for fetish objects. Some become aroused when they dress in sexy clothes, and the feel of fur next to the skin (e.g. making love on a fur rug or wearing a fur coat) will also arouse some women sexually.

Why should a man, and occasionally a woman, want to be tied up (or to tie up his or her partner) before he or she can become aroused?

Men and women who are unsure about their ability to make love may need some way to depersonalize their partner – that is, play down the emotions and play up the sex. A man, for example, who is an habitual visitor to prostitutes is often unable to cope with sex with a 'real' woman, but he becomes aroused with a prostitute partly because, by paying her, he has satisfied his need to please her and can then relax sufficiently to become sexually aroused. Similarly a man who enjoys being tied up by his partner or finds a woman who is prepared to be tied up by him, can, by ritualizing the relationship in this way, remove some of the 'person' from the sex act. If he is restrained, however lightly, it will help him to off-load on to the woman some of the responsibility for what happens between them, and he can then give himself 'permission' to be sexual because he is not under pressure to please her. Similarly, if she is tied up, she will then also become less of a person to him and hence more sexy.

What is sadomasochistic behaviour?

Strictly speaking, sadomasochists are those men and women who cannot become fully aroused sexually unless they either administer punishment (*sadism*) or receive it (*masochism*). Sometimes the sexual element is so deeply inhibited that all that remains is the need for violence and pain.

A fairly common and harmless form of *sadomasochism* is found, for example, in those who enjoy spanking, scratching or biting. Indeed, spanking is one of the few paraphilias that women admit to engaging in and enjoying. Usually punishment is administered by the palm of the hand, but sometimes canes or whips are used. Sex and aggression are obviously closely linked as is sex and punishment; it is therefore not difficult to see how spanking can become a regular part of love-making, with either partner playing the submissive role.

One of the problems with this kind of unusual sex is that, sooner or later, either the man or the woman will tire of the games, become restless and look elsewhere for their kicks. These rituals may even escalate into violence or more dangerous sexual activities. Relationships where unusual sex is an important feature are therefore likely to be more unstable than usual.

Why should a man want to dress up as a woman?
'Cross-dressing', or 'transvestism', is a well-known paraphilia, although the reasons why it is so pleasurable to some men may be very difficult to understand. A subtle kind of cross-dressing, which may provide some insight into this, would be, for example, where a man wears his wife's panties to work and finds that, as a result, he is sexually aroused all day. At this level, this kind of behaviour is probably no more than a clothes fetish, but transvestitism proper has much more to it than that.

Transvestites are often sexually aroused when they dress up, and they enjoy masturbating while cross-dressing. However, they also speak of a deep sense of tranquillity, of being at peace with themselves at this time, which would suggest a powerful emotional reward as well. Transvestites are rarely homosexual, are married and they live out fairly conventional lifestyles. Their children learn to accept that Daddy dresses up sometimes and usually attach very little importance to it.

Taken to an extreme, transvestism can become *transsexualism*, when a man really wants to become a woman and seeks hormone treatment and, ultimately, surgery. Most transvestites are, however, quite happy just cross-dressing from time to time, and certainly have no wish to change sex.

A man's need to cross-dress is not easy to explain, but in part, it is an expression of his dissatisfaction with his gender identity and gender role – that is, his self-image as a man and the role he is expected to play in the big world outside. At time, he feels he must escape these pressures and try to get closer to the feminine part of himself – hence the sense of peace (and also sexual arousal) so often experienced in cross-dressing. Just as some homosexuals have used the gay life as a way of opting out of the male sexual rat race, so transvestites use cross-dressing to achieve that goal but by a different route. More rarely, women cross-dress for the same reason: they, too, feel unhappy with their gender identity and role. However, many of these women, unlike male transvestites, are lesbians.

What is a paedophile?
Paedophilia literally means 'lover of children', but the word is usually used to describe those men (and, rarely, women) who seek physical contact with and sexual enjoyment from children of either sex. Probably about 10 per cent of all children can remember receiving the welcome or unwelcome sexual attentions of an adult, and not surprisingly, in some cases (though certainly not all), long-term damage can result, particularly if the adult–child relationship had gone on for a long time.

Society holds very strong views about this kind of behaviour (as it does about child pornography), but the true *paedophile* is very rarely a dangerous person; on the contrary, he is likely to be kind and loving, but like many others who engage in unusual sex, he is sexually inadequate and insecure. As a result of having this kind of personality he finds that he cannot form relationships with adults and breaks out of the rat race by turning to children because they are 'more approachable'. Research[41] has shown that paedophile men are often more sensitive and shy than other men – they could almost be described as children themselves.

Is prostitution a genuine example of 'unusual sex' in women?

This is not an easy question to answer because the reasons why a woman become a prostitute will depend upon her circumstances. There are obviously some women who 'go on the game' simply for the money, and their feelings towards men and sex are probably not particularly different from those of non-prostitutes – they are simply driven to it by poverty (in the same way that a man might have a homosexual relationship in prison because he is the victim of circumstance rather than because he is naturally gay). Young girls who get temporarily caught up in prostitution – perhaps for fun, or because their friends do it, or because it is simply a way of continuing a fairly normal promiscuous life but getting paid for it, or as a form of protest – provide a good example of this type of prostitution, and there is probably nothing very 'unusual' about these mildly delinquent young women's sex lives.

There are, however, some women for whom prostitution is, at least for a few years or even longer, a way of life. They are 'the naturals', and their promiscuous lifestyle is often the only way they can relate to men sexually. Like her customers, this kind of woman will find it very difficult to package love and sex together in one relationship, and her feelings towards men will be very ambivalent. She wants to be loved and therefore wants to please men, yet at the same time, she hates them, perhaps because they seem to enjoy sex more than she does, but more probably because she believes that she was never loved by her father, who may have been very rejecting, even violent. Any girl who has had this kind of turbulent relationship with her father is likely to have an unsettled sex life as an adult; add to this a greater-than-average aggressiveness, a desire for risk-taking and a need for sexual variety, perhaps as a necessary means of becoming aroused, and you have the ingredients for a prostitute. Just as many promiscuous men who have a Don Juan lifestyle are looking for a 'sexual mother', so some prostitutes are seeking a 'sexual father'. But, of course, neither can exist since they are contradictions: hence the length of the search, which can – and, in some cases, does – take a lifetime.

We are not for one moment trying to suggest that there are two types of prostitute; the 'economic' and 'psychological' explanations probably apply to a greater or lesser degree to all female prostitutes. Nor should it be thought that most prostitutes are miserable, exploited women who have been forced into this kind of slavery in order to survive. Most are fairly well-adjusted, happy women who enjoy their work. Money is certainly important, but the motive is often to get rich rather than to avoid starvation. Of course, some prostitutes are exploited and physically abused by pimps, and this totally unacceptable aspect of prostitution should not be overlooked.

How common are these unusual behaviours?
Very little is known about the numbers of people who *regularly* depend on unusual sex as their main source of arousal, because if questioned about their interest in the paraphilias, most people would deny any personal knowledge of them. One way to obtain some kind of estimate would be to look at the numbers of men who seek help from psychologists or sex therapists for this kind of problem (women rarely, if ever, seek treatment

for paraphilias) and also to count the number of prosecutions for those paraphilias that are against the law. However, the biggest obstacle to estimating the extent of unusual sex is our inability to categorize people.

One man in five, if not more, would probably admit to having enjoyed, at least on one occasion, being a voyeur, playing sex games involving cross-dressing, bondage or mild sadomasochism, but this does not make him a devotee of those particular paraphilias. Falling back, therefore, on what is no more than an intelligent guess, it is likely that the total number of men who are largely dependent on some form of unusual sex does not exceed the number of those who are exclusively gay; this would put the upper limit at about one in 40.

Is there any cure or help available for those men and women who wish to change their habits and give up unusual sex?

For many years now, psychologists and psychiatrists have been searching for ways by which they can help those people (particularly men) who find their lives being destroyed by their compelling need for unusual sex. The task has proved very difficult, and sometimes the only approach is to help the person to accept the fact that he has an obsessional need for whatever sexual ritual he has chosen and to learn to live with this. When the behaviour involves a confrontation with the law, this type of counselling obviously cannot be used, but most of the paraphilias are quite within the law; indeed, many organizations have been set up to counsel and provide introductions to other practitioners (see Chapter 10).

Behaviour therapy has been tried to help those who want to change their sexual habits, but in the main, the results have been rather disappointing. For example, *aversion therapy* (see p. 118) has been used with some success with transvestites, paedophiles, fetishists and sadomasochists, but often the changes in behaviour that take place are only temporary. More likely to work well are programmes that encourage paedophiles, for example, to develop more effective social skills. By becoming more assertive, they begin to feel more positive about themselves and are less likely to indulge in their particular paraphilias. Programmes such as these have been successful, but they are difficult and expensive to organise and can only be expected to help a very few people. In cases where harm is likely to befall either the man himself or another person, there may be little choice left but to fall back on a custodial sentence.

Is the incidence of paraphilias likely to increase in frequency?

Almost certainly not. As modern society becomes more understanding, and the often harmless nature of these usually quite private behaviours is recognized, many of these paraphilias will become totally accepted and of no social consequence.

Nowadays children are enjoying a more relaxed and positive attitude towards sex as they grow up, and the sense of guilt and shame, which has played such a big part in the past in creating these sexual problems, is slowly disappearing. Although it is difficult to prove, there is some evidence that these changes are already well underway. For example, the numbers of men who request specialist help from prostitutes to satisfy their unusual needs has probably diminished considerably; the rack, a frame to which some prostitutes used to tie their clients, is now relatively rare.

Is there a particular type of man who is more at risk of developing a need for unusual sex?

Although those who engage in the paraphilias have much in common, clearly it would be wrong to try to seek one simple answer to explain them all. The little research that has been done[42], however, suggests that

many of these men are more introverted (shy) and
anxious than average. If, in addition, this kind of
personality profile happens to be combined with a
precocious awareness of sex, perhaps a higher-than-
average sex drive and possibly a strict upbringing,
these might be the most likely ingredients that would
point men in the direction of unusual sex.

However, this is far from the whole story. There are
probably undiscovered biological reasons why strange
sex is so compelling to some. For example, some
transvestites have abnormal brain waves as measured
by an *electroencephalograph* (EEG)[43], thus providing
possible evidence of a physical explanation for their
behaviour. However, trans-sexuals and transvestites
appear to differ from those who indulge in the other
paraphilias because they are reported to have a *lower*
sex drive than average, so other explanations need to
be found to explain these behaviours.

Another characteristic that is often found in men and
women who enjoy unusual sex (in particular, voyeurs,
exhibitionists and paedophiles) is that they appear to
be aroused not so much by what they do but by the
fear of being discovered. It is the bittersweet
experience of anxiety that provides the real turn on[44].

**Even if some people are 'offended', does it matter
very much if some people are allowed to go ahead
and enjoy unusual sex as long as it does not hurt
anyone?**
On the face of it, the answer to this question appears to
be that it does not matter as long as no one comes to
any harm. However, in practice, it is very difficult to
express sexual needs, conventional or otherwise,
without involving another person. If a man lives on his
own and the behaviour is a private one, or he uses the
specialized services of a prostitute, there appears to be
no problem. However, in cases where the man has a
relationship with a woman, this may be jeopardized;
occasionally, children are put at risk; and the financial

resources of the family may be threatened, particularly if a criminal offence is committed. One of the authors can recall two men who sought help because they were spending thousands of pounds a year on prostitutes and were getting themselves into debt as a result.

What does a woman do if she finds out too late that she is married to a man who is into unusual sex?

If what he gets up is not a criminal offence, it remains simply a private matter between them both. For example, many transvestites are happily married men, and some wives are quite prepared to go through the sexual rituals that their husbands request from them for many years. However, in general, unusual sex places a lot of strain upon a relationship, and the wives find themselves quite unable or unwilling to go through the motions of dressing up, spanking or going with other men simply to arouse their husbands. Ultimately they find these practices offensive, depersonalized and, above all, unloving.

One of the authors had a patient who could only make love while his wife smoked a cigarette. At first, there was no problem, and she was happy to please him in this way, but eventually, she got fed up with what appeared to her to be a crazy idea and refused to smoke any more. The relationship foundered as a result.

More important is the fact that men with a need for unusual sex often themselves tire quickly of their own rituals and seek variety with other partners, with the inevitable result that the marriage is threatened. This may not mean that such a man has ceased to 'love' his wife, but that he is quite unable to express love and sex together in one relationship. She, however, does not see it in quite the same way, and finding the relationship increasingly intolerable, she eventually walks out.

134

9.
SEX AND THE LAW

There are at least 25 separate Acts of Parliament, apart from common law, which set out to regulate the way men and women behave sexually. Some of these laws are very complicated and difficult to interpret, even by lawyers. This brief chapter seeks only to provide an introduction to this vast subject and anyone in need of professional advice should consult a solicitor. Much of what is written here applies only to England and Wales; laws relating to Scotland and Northern Ireland may be different.

What is the law relating to incest?
It is an offence for a man to have intercourse with a woman whom he knows to be his daughter, mother, sister, half-sister or granddaughter. It is also an offence for a woman to have intercourse with her father, grandfather, brother, half-brother or son. Under the Sexual Offences Act, 1956 the penalties vary from two years to life imprisonment.

What is rape and how does the law deal with offenders?
It is a criminal offence for a man to have intercourse with a woman without her consent. This is rape. The man does not have to ejaculate but simply to penetrate the vagina with his penis. Although there have been moves to change things, at the moment a man cannot

normally be charged with raping his wife unless there is a court order relating to separation or divorce: a woman can also refuse sexual intercourse with her husband under civil law if he has been guilty of a matrimonial offence or because he is suffering from a sexually transmitted disease. Attempted rape and aiding and abetting rape are also serious offences. Rape is dealt with by a number of statutes (the Sexual Offences Acts, 1956, 1976, 1985) and has a maximum penalty of life imprisonment. Normally nothing may be published which would lead to either the victim or the offender being identified while a trial is in progress; however, on conviction, the name of the rapist can be made public, but not that of the victim. There is amending legislation (the Criminal Justice Bill, 1988) going through Parliament at the time of writing which would remove the protection of anonymity from the offender entirely.

On what other occasions, apart from rape, is intercourse unlawful?

There are a number of circumstances when intercourse is against the law. For example, it is an offence under the Sexual Offences Act, 1956 for a man to have (or attempt to have) intercourse with a girl under the age of 16 – unless, and only if, he is under 24 himself and has not been previously charged with this offence, and also genuinely believes the girl is over 16. Apart from this exception the maximum penalty for this offence is two years imprisonment. It is also against the law for a man to give a woman any drugs specifically in order to achieve intercourse – that is drugs which, if taken by her, would affect her capacity to be responsible for her actions. Heterosexual anal intercourse is also against the law in any circumstances, even between husband and a consenting wife, even though probably as many as one in five women report enjoying anal sex[45]. This particular section of the Sexual Offences Act is however rarely invoked.

What is an indecent assault?

This is a phrase which is often used in the media but, for obvious reasons, is rarely defined, (even the Act of Parliament itself doesn't define what is meant by indecent assault). In practice an 'indecent assault' refers to any sexual behaviour which takes place between a man and a woman without the consent of one and which falls short of actual intercourse. Obviously, if a man pinches a woman's bottom or kisses her neck, for example, this would probably not amount to an assault but would be regarded as sexual harassment, which is not yet a criminal offence. However, if he were to put his hand under her clothing to feel her breasts, or up her skirt this would certainly be regarded as an indecent assault as it would be if a man forced a woman to give him oral sex or masturbated and ejaculated on her body. All forms of indecent behaviour of this kind are unlawful and the only defence a man can have (if she is over the age of 16) is that the woman consented to it: indeed, a man can be prosecuted for indecently assaulting his wife. An act of gross indecency takes place between two men if their behaviour departs from that which is lawful as defined in the Sexual Offences Act, 1967 (see below).

When is a woman entitled to a legal abortion?

Abortion is legal if two doctors independently come to the conclusion that a pregnant woman is at some kind of risk should her pregnancy continue. The risks that the Abortion Act, 1967 recognize are: a risk to the life of the pregnant woman, that her physical or mental health is threatened or that of her existing children, or that there is a substantial risk that the child, if it were born, would be seriously handicapped either physically or mentally. In practice the Abortion Act is interpreted compassionately by most doctors, although it does fall short of abortion on demand. A woman may have a legal abortion without her husband's consent or knowledge, as may a girl over 16 without her parent's consent.

The termination can only be carried out if the pregnancy has lasted no more than 28 weeks; after this the offence of 'child destruction' may be committed. This is covered by the Infant Life Preservation Act, 1929 where the destruction of a viable foetus is only allowed to save the life of the mother. An abortion can only be performed in a National Health Service hospital or in one of a number of specially approved nursing homes where a fee would be charged: in 1989 this was about £160 for a termination up to 16 weeks, and for those between 16 and 24 weeks the cost would be about £300 because more sophisticated procedures are necessary. At the time of writing, there is an agreement between the Department of Health and all the private nursing homes licensed to do abortions that the latter will not terminate pregnancies later than 24 weeks.

The Abortion Act, 1967 does not apply to Northern Ireland where an abortion is only allowed on medical grounds or if the mother is mentally handicapped. It is, of course, totally unlawful in the Republic of Ireland.

What will happen to a man if he exposes himself – that is displays his penis in front of a woman with the intention of upsetting her?
The Town Police Clauses Act, 1847 and the Vagrancy Act, 1824 are used to prosecute exhibitionists. In what is now picturesque language, they make it an offence for a man 'to wilfully, openly, lewdly and obscenely expose his person with intent to insult any female'. The maximum penalty is a £400 fine or three months imprisonment.

First offenders may not be prosecuted, but simply given a warning, or they may be 'bound over to keep the peace' or advised to seek psychiatric treatment. If the offence is repeated they will certainly be punished and may be fined or even sent to prison. The frequency of this kind of offence has dropped considerably since video-porn has become more freely available but habitual (recidivist) offenders are commonplace.

What does the law have to say about sexual contact between humans and other animals?
Under the Sexual Offences Acts, 1956 and 1967 it is an offence for man to commit 'buggery' with an animal. It is not clear from this act what buggery actually means though case law does describe buggery as anal intercourse. This piece of legislation is rarely enforced nowadays, though the maximum penalty still remains as life imprisonment.

It is said that homosexual behaviour is now legal – is this true?
All homosexual behaviour between men, that is acts of gross indecency (behaviour falling short of anal intercourse) and 'buggery' itself, are still against the law except when both men are over the age of 21, they both consent, and it is done in private (Sexual Offences Act, 1967). This means that if more than two men are present it is still against the law. Also, homosexual contact is prohibited in public lavatories, by crews on merchant ships and in the armed services. An offence of 'buggery', as the law so delicately puts it, is variously punished: with a boy of under 16, life imprisonment; with a man of 16 or more without his consent, 10 years; and 2 to 5 years for less serious offences.

Homosexual behaviour between women is lawful in all circumstances, as long as those involved can and do consent to it.

Has female circumcision – that is the ritual mutilation of the sexual organs of a woman – now become an offence?
Yes, as recently as 1985. The Prohibition of Female Circumcision Act makes it an offence to do any surgery on the vulva of a woman unless it is medically

necessary. It is no defence to argue that it is part of a religious custom or ritual. The maximum penalty is an unspecified fine, five years' imprisonment or both.

What is a surrogate mother and is it legal to be one?

A surrogate mother is a woman who has agreed to have a baby which she has promised in advance to hand over to another, usually childless, person together with all her rights in that child. A fee and expenses are usually paid to her for this undertaking. This is legal but the Surrogacy Arrangements Act, 1985 makes it illegal for a third party – for instance, an agency, doctor or, indeed, any person, professional or otherwise – to obtain any financial reward for arranging these introductions. It is also an offence for a newspaper, or any other publication, to accept an advertisement from anyone which might result in a contract between a prospective surrogate mother and any other person. The maximum penalty is a fine of £2000 or three months' imprisonment or both.

Is prostitution legal?

The answer to this question highlights the unique art of British compromise. Only in Britain could there be a law which allows prostitution itself to be a lawful activity and yet which makes the life of the prostitute and her clients intolerable by making it almost impossible for the two ever to get together without breaking the law. It is rather like having thousands of fully stocked unlicensed public houses and an awful lot of thirsty customers.

Under the Sexual Offences Acts, 1956, 1967 and 1985 and the Street Offences Act, 1959 the situation is this. A prostitute can advertise, but strictly speaking no one can accept her advertisement. She can work lawfully in a brothel yet no one is allowed to run a brothel. She can charge for her services yet no one can live off her earnings. She can ply her trade but no one can procure her to do so. She can see her customers in her own home but she must not appear at a window or a door to let them know she is there. She must not seek her clients in public places nor can anyone seek her in public places. The resource she seeks to sell is lawful, yet it is virtually unobtainable lawfully.

Do sex shops have to be licensed?

There are sex shops and sex shops. For example, a sex shop that sells anything from sexy lingerie and 'aphrodisiac' herb pills to vibrators and inflatable dolls does not require a licence – it only has to conform to local planning laws and consents by councils cannot be unreasonably withheld. However, sex shops that sell books, magazines, films and in particular 18R (restricted) videos (see below) do require a licence under the Local Government (Miscellaneous Provisions) Act, 1982 as of course do sex cinemas where these films and videos can legally be shown commercially.

Can sexually explicit pornographic videos be bought legally from a shop?

The Video Recordings Act, 1984 lays down that all English language videos must be classified by the British Board of Film Classification. However, there are two exceptions to this rule. The first exception is where the videos are *exempted works* – that is, those that are educational, religious, or video games (however, videos that show any sexually explicit sequences cannot be classified as 'educational' even if that is their purpose). The second exception is where the videos qualify as being *exempted supplies*. This applies when the video is provided for use in the training or practice of a limited number of professions such as medicine, nursing, psychotherapy and so on. In every other instance videos must be licenced and classified into one of the following categories:

UC Universal: particularly suitable for children

141

U   Universal: suitable for everyone

PG   Parental Guidance: some scenes may be unsuitable for children

15   Suitable for those 15 or over; not to be sold or hired to anyone under 15

18   Suitable only for those 18 or over; not to be sold or hired to anyone under 18

18R   Restricted. Only supplied in licensed sex shops to anyone 18 or over

It is under the last category – 18R – that sexually explicit pornography may be purchased quite legally from sex shops. However, in addition there remains a flourishing black market in video-porn which will doubtless continue for as long as there is a demand. The penalty for being in breach of this law is a fine of up to £20,000.

How does the law influence the availability of pornography?

The debate over what is and what is not pornography has raged for centuries and the debate continues unchecked. First, no one appears to have been able to provide a satisfactory definition of obscenity. This is not surprising since 'one man's porn is another man's corn'. The Obscene Publications Act, 1959 defines 'obscene' highly unsatisfactorily as anything that tends to deprave and corrupt those who are likely to read, see or hear it – a proposition that is incapable of any proof other than 'I find it offensive'. Juries clearly have great difficulty with this test of obscenity and not infrequently accept 'not guilty' pleas despite an apparently convincing case for the prosecution. Apart from the subjective nature of any definition of obscenity there is the inescapable fact that many of the things that were regarded as 'obscene', say, 30 years ago are now seen to be acceptable.

There is a legal defence against the charge of obscenity. It can be set aside if it can be shown that the material is for the public good on the grounds that it is in the interests of science, literature, art and learning.

Other Acts of Parliament which do not have this means of defence deal with special situations. For example, the Post Office Act, 1953 prohibits the use of the post to transmit any indecent material of whatever nature. The contents of plays is controlled by the Theatres Act, 1968 which prohibits the performance of an 'obscene' play and the Cable and Broadcasting Act, 1984 covers the transmission of indecent and obscene matter by cable. The Indecent Displays (Control) Act, 1982 serves to prevent shops displaying indecent material such as the covers of sexually explicit 'girly' magazines and finally the Customs Consolidation Act, 1876 prohibits the importation of indecent and obscene material of any kind through Her Majesty's Customs.

Is 'child pornography' dealt with by the courts?
Under the Protection of Children Act, 1978 it is an offence to take photographs and make videos or films of children under the age of 16 which might be regarded as being 'indecent'. 'Indecent' is not defined, but the courts would doubtless regard a charge of indecency easier to establish than one of obscenity. For example, even a collection of simple poses of naked boys and girls could be in breach of this Act. It is also an offence under this Act to distribute, show or have in one's possession material of this kind. The maximum penalty for an offence under this Act is three years' imprisonment or an unspecified fine, or both.

Is it an offence to make an obscene telephone call?
The Telecommunications Act, 1984 makes it an offence to use a public telephone system to send a grossly offensive, indecent, obscene or menacing message. The maximum penalty is a £400 fine.

How do the laws concerning sexual behaviour affect people with a mental handicap?

A number of Acts of Parliament, but in particular the Sexual Offences Act, 1956 and the various Mental Health Acts, lay down the rules governing sex and people with a mental handicap. Generally speaking men and women who have a mental handicap – for example those who suffer from Down's Syndrome or who have an inherited biochemical disorder that has resulted in the brain failing to develop normally – have the same rights as anyone else. For example, with parents consent they can get married at 16 (even detained patients can marry in hospital); they can also get divorced.

However, it is unlawful for a *man* to have intercourse with a woman who has a mental handicap unless it can be argued that he wasn't aware that she was handicapped; she cannot have intercourse with anyone unless she is married and then only with her husband. On the other hand, a man with a mental handicap can have intercourse with anyone else (except a woman with a mental handicap) because the law only discriminates against (or protects) women. It is a serious offence to *procure* a woman with mental handicap for the purpose of prostitution or to commit an indecent assault on her and it is also an offence for any man to have any homosexual contact with another man who has a mental handicap.

There are calls for a change in the law so that sex is possible between men and women, who both have a mental hanciap as long as it can be established that they are both consenting.

10.
WHERE TO GO FOR HELP

Nowadays, there are many people and organizations readily available for those who need advice and help with a sexual problem. Sometimes it takes a lot of courage to share this kind of problem with a stranger, but if the situation is sufficiently distressing, the sooner help is obtained, the more likely a solution will be found.

YOUR FAMILY DOCTOR

If you go and see your GP about a sexual problem or an emotional problem related to sex, what happens next will depend on where you live. Most National Health Service regions have hospital-based clinics where specialists can deal with most sexual difficulties. However, in some areas (largely because of shortage of funds), this type of referral is not always easy because of the long waiting lists. Instead, your GP will refer you either to the Family Planning Association or to Relate (formerly the National Marriage Guidance Council). Very occasionally, family doctors themselves may be prepared to help.

Do try to remember that it is often a very good idea to talk to your GP first, if only because he or she will know about the local helping agencies in your area.

ORGANIZATIONS

Mainly for women
British Pregnancy Advisory Service (BPAS), Austy
Manor, Wootton Wawen, Solihull, West Midlands
B95 6DA. Tel: (056 42) 3225
A national organization set up particularly to help
women who are seeking advice on abortion. They also
deal with psychosexual problems.

Brook Advisory Centres, 153a East St, London
SE17 2SD. Tel: (01) 708 1234/1390 (information);
(01) 703 9660/7880 (clinic)
A national organization specifically set up to help
young people with sexual and emotional problems and,
in particular, to provide contraception and infection
testing when needed. They have a number of branches
throughout the country.

Family Planning Association/Information Service,
St Andrew's House, 27–35 Mortimer St, London
W1N 7RJ. Tel: (01) 636 7866
The Family Planning Association have clinics
throughout the country offering help to those with
sexual and emotional problems in addition to its
fertility-control work. It is probably best to contact
your local branch (look in the Yellow Pages under
'Family Planning'). Alternatively, ring the Family
Planning Information Service; they will tell you where
the nearest clinic is located, and can also provide
information and leaflets on a great number of relevant
subjects.

Marie Stopes Clinic, 108 Whitfield St, London
W1P 6BE. Tel: (01) 388 0662
The eight Marie Stopes clinics throughout the country
provide practical help and advice on all forms of
fertility control. There is a charge for treatment.

National Association for Pre-menstrual Syndrome (NAPS), 6 Beech Lane, Guildown, Guildford, Surrey GU2 5ES
Offer advice for women with PMS; especially concerned with hormone therapy.

Women's Nutritional Advice Service, PO Box 268, Brighton, East Sussex BN3 1RW. Tel: (0273) 771366
A postal advisory service dealing with women's problems in general and pre-menstrual tension and menopause in particular.

Sex therapy and psychotherapy
Association of Sexual and Marital Therapists, PO Box 62, Sheffield S10 3TL
Professional body to which most qualified sex therapists belong. The Association holds a list of approved therapists throughout the country and will send this to those who request it. The members of the Association work both for the NHS and privately.

British Association for Counselling, 37a Sheep St, Rugby CV21 3BX. Tel: (0788) 78328/9
If you have difficulty establishing contact with a therapist or counsellor, the BAC may be able to put you in touch with one near your home. They also publish a directory of all organizations in the British Isles providing help for psychosexual problems.

Institute of Psychosexual Medicine, 11 Chandos St, Cavendish Sq., London W1M 9DE. Tel: (01) 580 1043
A group of medical practitioners specializing in the treatment of sexual problems, particularly in women.

National Association of Young People's Counselling and Advisory Services, 17–23 Albion St, Leicester LE1 6GD. Tel: (0533) 558763
If you are young and cannot find a counselling centre, this organization will put you in touch with the one nearest you.

147

Relate: National Marriage Guidance (formerly
National Marriage Guidance Council), Herbert Gray
College, Little Church St, Rugby CV21 3AP. Tel:
(0788) 73241
Relate has over 500 centres throughout the United
Kingdom; their addresses and telephone numbers can
be found in local telephone directories. In about 90
towns and cities, there are also special MST (marital
and sexual therapy) clinics, which specialize in the
treatment of those with sexual problems. Although this
is a voluntary organization, contributions from clients
are appreciated and needed to help with the cost of
running the clinics.

Helplines
Childline, Freepost 1111, London EC4B 4BB. Tel:
(0800) 1111
Helpline for children who are, or are frightened of,
being sexually and/or physically abused.

Healthline. Tel: (01) 980 4848 (2–10 pm); Basingstoke
(0256) 471438; Croydon (01) 681 3311; Exeter (0392)
59191; Hull (0482) 29933.
A comprehensive advisory service run by the College of
Health comprising over 200–6-minute tapes on a wide
range of problems: medical, sexual and emotional. The
only cost is the price of the telephone call.

Incest Crisis Line, Tel: (01) 422 5100 or (01) 890 4732
Offers counselling and support for adults and young
people who may be victims of incest or abuse.

For the single, separated, divorced or widowed
While the organizations listed below are not
specifically concerned with providing treatment for
sexual problems, they are included here because, so
often, the solution to a sexual difficulty depends on the
formation of a mutually rewarding relationship.

Cruse, Cruse House, 126 Sheen Rd, Richmond, Surrey TW9 1UR. Tel: (01) 940 4818/9047
National organization set up to counsel and offer practical advice to those who have been bereaved; has many local branches.

Gingerbread, 35 Wellington St, London WC2E 7BN. Tel: (01) 240 0953
National network of self-help groups for one-parent families.

National Council for One-Parent Families, 255 Kentish Town Rd, London NW5 2LX. Tel: (01) 267 1361
Provides information, advice and counselling for one-parent families.

National Federation of Solo Clubs, Room 8, Ruskin Chambers, 191 Corporation St, Birmingham B4 6RY. Tel: (021) 236 2879
Social clubs throughout the country for the single, separated, divorced or widowed. All ages welcome.

Singles, 23 Abingdon Rd, London W8 6AH. Tel: (01) 938 1011
Excellent and reputable dating magazine.

Miscellaneous
Beaumont Society, Box BM 3084, London WC1N 3XX
Provides information, support and contacts for transvestites and trans-sexuals.

Friend, 274 Upper St, London N1 2UA or Box BM Friend, London WC1N 3XX. Tel: (01) 837 3337
National network of groups that provide help for gay people of either sex.

Outsiders Club, Box 4ZB, London W1A 4ZB. Tel: (01) 499 0900
Support group for the physically handicapped who are seeking relationships.

SHAFT (Self-Help Association for Trans-sexuals),
106 Barton Ave, Keyham, Plymouth PL2 1NZ. Tel:
(0752) 559939
Self-help group for transsexuals and those who think
they may be.

**SPOD: Association to Aid the Sexual and Personal
Relationships of People with a Disability**, 286
Camden Rd, London N7 0BJ. Tel: (01) 607 8851/2
Helps those who are either physically or mentally
handicapped. SPOD will put you in touch, whenever
possible, with a local counsellor if you have difficulty
finding one.

Terrence Higgins Trust, 52/54 Gray's Inn Rd, London
WC1X 8JU. Tel: (01) 242 1010 (3–10 pm, everyday)
A charity set up to provide information, advice and
support for those who are worried about HIV infection
and AIDS.

Further information
A comprehensive guide for those who need help with a
sexual or emotional problem is provided by Ann
Darnborough and Derek Kinrade in *The Sex Directory*
(Cambridge, Woodhead-Faulkner, 1988). This book lists
a wide range of helping agencies in the UK, and
readers are strongly recommended to consult it if they
cannot find appropriate help in any other way.

FURTHER READING

Many bookshops display a multitude of books about sex, some of which are very good and others are not. Those listed here are, in the authors' opinion, some of the best. Consulting a well-written book can do two things: it can provide a source of useful information, and it can help to put whatever the problem is in its proper perspective so that sensible decisions can be made about whether or not to seek help.

Sex education and general

Jane Cousins, *Make It Happy: what sex is all about*, London, Penguin, 1980.
For teenagers who want to learn about sex.

James Docherty, *Growing Up*, Modus Books, 1986.
An introduction to sex education for adolescents, with a lot of explicit photographs. Suitable for most ages.

W.H. Masters, V.E. Johnson & R.C. Kolodny, *Sex and Human Loving*, London, Macmillan, 1986.
This publication is both a reference book and a very readable account of every imaginable kind of sex and loving. It is factually sound, well written and strongly recommended as an 'intelligent person's guide'.

Susan Meredith, *Understanding the Facts of Life*, London, Usborne, 1985.
A useful and well-illustrated book (drawings, not photographs) produced for boys and girls of about the age of puberty onwards.

Claire Rayner, *Lifeguide*, London, NEL, 1980.
A reference book providing sound advice on every imaginable medical and emotional problem, but with a large section on sex and relationships.

Kaye Wellings, *First Love, First Sex – a practical guide to relationships*, Wellingborough, Thorsons, 1986.
Well-illustrated introduction specifically written for young people.

Dilys Went, *Sex Education: some guidelines for teachers*, London, Bell & Hyman (now Unwin Hyman), 1985.
Written mainly for teachers, although many others could benefit from reading it. The subject is presented in an objective but sensitive manner, avoiding the pitfalls that sometimes bedevil books on sex education.

Sexual and relationship problems

Paul Brown & Caroline Faulder, *Treat Yourself to Sex*, London, Penguin, 1979.
Explains how to understand and help yourself with common sex problems.

Alex Comfort, *The Joy of Sex*, London, Mitchell Beazley, 1986 and *More Joy of Sex*, London, Quartet Books, 1977.
Two very good, well-illustrated books containing a wealth of information and providing an excellent introduction to sex.

David Delvin, *The Book of Love*, 1974 and *How to Improve Your Sex Life*, 1987, both London, NEL.
Two comprehensive books on sex and love-making, which also mention contraception, sexually transmitted diseases, pregnancy and abortion.

John Hart, *So You Think You Are Attracted to the Same Sex*, London, Penguin, 1984.
The ideal book for young people who are unsure of their sexual feelings and believe that they may be gay.

Maurice Yaffé, *Sexual Happiness: a practical approach*, London, Dorling Kindersley, 1986.
A very well-produced illustrated book on how to get the most out of sex and relationships.

Mainly for women

Lonnie Barbach, *For Yourself: the fulfilment of female sexuality*, Signet, 1975.
A guide to help women achieve orgasm. Contains lots of practical exercises that women can carry out on their own.

For Each Other: sharing sexual intimacy, London Corgi, 1983.
Broader in scope than the above. Contains over 50 practical exercises that women can carry out on their own and with their partners.

David Delvin, *The* She *Complete Guide to Sex and Loving*, London, Ebury Press, 1986.
An illustrated account about everything you need to know. Well written and with a sense of humour.

Nancy Friday, *My Secret Garden*, London, Quartet Books, 1988.
A unique collection of women's sexual fantasies, which may prove very helpful for those women who want to understand more about their own sexual feelings.

Julia Heiman, Leslie LoPiccolo & Joseph LoPiccolo, *Becoming Orgasmic: a sexual growth program for women*, Englewood Cliffs, New Jersey, Prentice-Hall, 1986.
Covers ground similar to Lonnie Barbach's *For Yourself* but is more structured and easier to read.

Anne Hooper, *Women and Sex*, London, Sheldon Press, 1986.
Deals with most of the sexual problems that specially concern women.

153

Deidre Sanders, *The* Woman *Book of Love and Sex*, London, Sphere, 1985.
Book about women's sexual problems, based on a remarkable survey conducted by the author on women's sexual attitudes and behaviour.

Mainly for men

Deidre Sanders, *The* Woman *Report on Men*, London, Sphere Books, 1987.
Companion volume to the above and also based on a large survey, on men's sexual behaviour and feelings.

Bernard Zilbergeld, *Men and Sex*, London, Fontana, 1980.
Any man who needs information on or is worried about a sexual problem should read this, as should women.

Special areas

V.G. Daniels, *AIDS – The Acquired Immune Deficiency Syndrome*, MTP Press, 1986.
A comprehensive and accurate guide to AIDS, providing an up-to-date, factual account of this disease.

Michael Haslam, *Deviant Sex Behaviour*, Oxford, Clarendon Press, 1974.
An introduction to sexual problems and so-called 'deviant' behaviours.

Paul Hauck, *Jealousy*, London, Sheldon Press, 1982.
A little book full of sound advice on how to cope with jealous feelings.

How to Love and Be Loved, London, Sheldon Press, 1983.
Another book full of common sense about relationships.

Derek Llewellyn-Jones, *Herpes, Aids and Other Sexually Transmitted Diseases*, London, Faber, 1985.
An up-to-date, well-written, comprehensive account of all the sexually transmitted diseases, together with advice on how they should be treated.

Elliot Philipp, *Safe Sex: the pleasures without the pitfalls*, London, Columbus Books (now Harrap Columbus), 1987.
An easy-to-understand account of the delights and hazards of sex – essential reading for the sexually active from the age of 13 years upwards.

Christine E. Sandford, *Enjoy Sex in the Middle Years*, London, Macdonald Optima, 1983.
As the title suggests, this book is directed towards those couples whose children are now growing up and who may need help with their own sexual and emotional problems in middle life.

General reference books

John Bancroft, *Human Sexuality and Its Problems*, Edinburgh, Churchill Livingstone, 1989.
Probably one of the best reference books available. Although quite technical in places, it is very comprehensive and indispensable both for the professional and for others.

Helen S. Kaplan, *The New Sex Therapy*, London, Ballière Tindall, 1974.
This book, which followed Masters and Johnson's *Human Sexual Inadequacy*, is an excellent reference text and adds a great deal to what was written earlier by those authors. Although not a recent publication, it remains an excellent introductory text for professionals.

W.H. Masters & V.E. Johnson, *Human Sexual Response*, Boston, Massachusetts, Little Brown, 1966 and *Human Sexual Inadequacy*, London, J. & A. Churchill, 1970.
Two books by these now well known authors which report on their pioneering work in sex therapy. The first describes the results of their research into the anatomy and physiology of human sexual behaviour and the second provides details of their methods of treating the common sex disorders.

J. Money & H. Musaph (eds), *Handbook of Sexology*,
Excerpta Medica, 1979.
A comprehensive handbook for reference purposes. A
little dated on the scientific side, but an excellent
publication, rather like an encyclopaedia and covering
the whole subject.

Books for doctors and other professionals

Martin Cole & Windy Dryden (eds), *Sex Therapy in
Britain*, Milton Keynes, Open University Press, 1988.
A comprehensive and up-to-date account of sex therapy
by leading British practitioners in their respective
fields.

Patricia Gillan, *The Sex Therapy Manual*, Oxford,
Blackwell Scientific, 1987.
An up-to-date account, focusing on group therapy.

Keith Hawton, *Sex Therapy – a practical guide*, Oxford
Medical Publications, 1985.
This is an easy-to-read, compact and comprehensive
introduction to sex therapy, written for those with a
professional interest in the subject.

Helen S. Kaplan, *The Evaluation of Sexual Disorders*,
Brunner/Mazel, 1983.
A comprehensive guide to the ways in which an
accurate diagnosis of most sexual disorders can be
undertaken.

Sex surveys

P.H. Gebhard & A.B. Johnson, *The Kinsey Data*,
London, W.B. Saunders, 1979.
The data collected by Kinsey and his colleagues are
here re-analysed and presented in the form of easily
understood tables.

Shere Hite, *The Hite Report*, London, Macmillan, 1976
and *The Hite Report on Male Sexuality*, London,
Macdonald, 1981.
Two excellent surveys of sexual behaviour which,

though sometimes criticized, have added considerably to our knowledge.

A.C. Kinsey and others, *Sexual Behavior in the Human Male*, 1948 and *Sexual Behavior in the Human Female*, 1953, both London, W.B. Saunders.
The monumental survey of human sexual behaviour: it still remains, many years later, the most valuable contribution to our understanding of the subject.

A. Pietropinto & J. Simenauer, *Beyond the Male Myth*, New York, Times Books, 1977.
A survey of the sexual behaviour of American males.

Michael Schofield, *The Sexual Behaviour of Young People*, Harlow, Longmans, 1965 and *The Sexual Behaviour of Young Adults*, Hamondsworth, Allen Lane (Penguin), 1973.
Two British publications that report on the sexual behaviour of the same young people at different times in their lives.

GLOSSARY

abortion   termination of pregnancy. This may be legal or illegal, spontaneous (a miscarriage) or induced deliberately.

adrenalin   hormone secreted by the adrenal glands. It prepares the body for 'fright or flight' by, among other things, raising the blood pressure and increasing the amount of sugar in the blood.

artificial insemination (AI)   process by which semen (containing sperm) is deposited in the vagina artificially via a tube and syringe. Either the semen of the husband is used (AIH) or that of an anonymous donor (AID).

aversion therapy   form of behaviour therapy, in which attempts are made to eliminate unwanted behaviours by associating them with unpleasant stimuli.

behaviour therapy   form of psychotherapy that focuses on the unwanted behaviour itself, attempts to modify or eliminate the unwanted behaviour by altering a person's lifestyle or by providing him or her with specific assignments and exercises – rather than by trying to understand the emotional conflicts that may have led to the behaviour.

bondage   practice of tying up or restraining one's sexual partner during love-making.

chordee   curvature of the penis when erect.

chromosome   thread-like structures found in the nuclei of most cells of the body, on which genetic (hereditary) information is coded in the genes.

circumcision   in the male, the surgical removal of the foreskin from the tip of the penis; in the female, the removal of various parts of the vulva, including the labia (lips) and the clitoris.

clitoris   small, erotically sensitive, erectile part of the vulva, found at the top where the lips meet.

clomipramine (trade name = Anafranil)   anti-depressant drug sometimes used in the treatment of premature ejaculation.

colostomy   surgical operation in which part of the large intestine (colon) is removed and an artificial opening is made in the abdomen to allow for the removal of solid waste products.

cross-dressing   see *transvestite*.

cunnilingus   oral sex in which a man or woman stimulates a woman's vulva with his or her mouth.

cystic fibrosis   inherited disease of the pancreas resulting in an abnormality of body secretions.

delayed ejaculation   relatively rare sexual disorder in which men find it difficult or impossible to reach orgasm and ejaculate.

dilators   glass or plastic tubes of graded sizes used in the treatment of vaginismus.

dildo   object that serves as a substitute for a penis.

dysfunction   disorder – e.g. erectile dysfunction where the penis fails to become erect.

dyspareunia   painful intercourse.

electroencephalograph (EEG)   instrument that measures electric impulses in the brain.

exhibitionist   men (and occasionally women) who have an often uncontrollable urge to display their sex organs in public.

fellatio   oral sex in which a man or a woman stimulates a man's penis with his or her mouth.

fetishist   man (or woman) who requires the presence of a particular object (such as a piece of clothing) before becoming sexually aroused.

foetus   unborn child developing in the uterus.

G-spot   erotically sensitive area inside the entrance to the vagina beneath the pubic region.

heterophobia   fear of the opposite sex.

hormone replacement therapy (HRT)   administration of a hormone to replace one that the body no longer produces in sufficient quantities itself. A well-known example of HRT is the replacement of *oestrogen* and *progesterone* in women after menopause.

hormones   specific 'chemical messengers' secreted by various glands in the body. This endocrine system serves to control the functions of other organs elsewhere in the body – e.g. insulin regulates the level of sugar in the body, and the female sex hormones *oestrogen* and *progesterone* control a woman's menstrual cycle.

hymen   perforated piece of skin encircling the entrance to the vagina.

hypnotherapy   treatment involving the use of hypnosis, in which a therapist induces a trance-like state in a person, which resembles sleep, by suggestion or other means.

hypothalamus   part of the brain, located at its base immediately above the pituitary gland, with which it shares the responsibility for regulating many bodily (and, particularly, sexual) functions.

ileostomy   artificial opening on the abdomen following surgery where the whole of the large bowel has to be removed.

imprinting   process of learning which takes place during a restricted period, often when the organism is very young.

incest   having sex with a member of one's own immediate family.

KY jelly   water-soluble jelly, readily available from chemists, which serves as an excellent lubricant during intercourse.

lubrication   in the context of sexual behaviour, secretion of often large amounts of clear liquid from the walls of the vagina in a sexually aroused woman.

masochism   see *sadomasochists*.

monoamine oxidase inhibitor (MAOI)   powerful anti-depressant drug.

Oedipus complex   particularly close attraction of a son to his mother (or daughter to father), which is said to result in emotional and sexual problems in later life.

oestrogen   one of the two hormones produced by the ovaries in a woman (men also produce small quantities). This hormone is responsible for the development and maintenance of the female sexual characteristics, together with a woman's normal sexual and reproductive functioning.

orgasm   peak of sexual excitement experienced by men and women when they masturbate or have intercourse.
experience for many women.

ovum   egg released from the ovaries at periodic intervals during a woman's reproductive life.

paedophile   man (or woman) who is sexually attracted to young children.

papaverine   drug that relaxes some muscles of the body and in particular those which surround the blood vessels, which become dilated as a result, hence it is used in the diagnosis and treatment of men with erectile difficulties.

paraphilia   'unusual love'. This includes sexual behaviour originally known as 'deviant' or 'perverted', but is here described as 'unusual sex'.

penile implant splint   usually two flexible or inflatable rods of plastic that are inserted surgically into the penis to provide an erection.

penis   external sex organ of the male: it comprises the shaft and the glans penis, its sensitive tip.

performance anxiety   self-fulfilling fears about (sexual) performance, resulting from past failures.

Peyronies disease   condition of the penis in which the presence of hard areas of tissue in the shaft causes curvature and pain on erection.

phentolamine   substance that dilates (widens) blood vessels; sometimes used in the treatment of men with erectile problems (see *papaverine*).

phenylephrine   drug that constricts blood vessels; used in the treatment of priapism.

pheromones   substances often found in the urine and secretions of the sexual organs, which produce changes in the social and sexual behaviour of the same species. For example, a pheromone in the male dog's urine will serve to mark out his territory, and that in the urine of a bitch will act as a sexual attractant. Pheromones are normally perceived by the sense of smell.

pituitary gland   ductless gland found just under the brain, and controlled by the *hypothalamus*; it produces many important hormones, some of which control the activity of other glands of the endocrine system.

placebo effect   often beneficial effect of prescribing a harmless and inactive substance to a patient, who believes that the medication is potent.

placenta   afterbirth; structure through which the developing foetus receives oxygen and nourishment from its mother and excretes its waste products.

premature ejaculation   common sexual problem in men, where orgasm and ejaculation are reached very quickly via either masturbation or intercourse.

priapism   unwanted erection of the penis in the absence of sexual stimulation, which persists for several hours or even longer.

progesterone   hormone secreted by the ovaries and which is responsible for preparing the lining of the uterus for a pregnancy.

prostaglandins   substances found throughout the body, which perform a number of different functions but in particular lead to the contraction of the muscles of the uterus.

prostatectomy   surgical removal of part or all of a man's prostate gland.

prostate gland   gland found at the base of a man's bladder, which is about the size of a chestnut. It is partly responsible for the production of the semen in which sperm are ejaculated.

psychoanalysis   form of psychotherapy that assumes that disordered behaviour is caused largely by the existence of unconscious (and often deeply repressed) conflicts and drives that arose early in childhood. Treatment depends on the establishment of a special relationship with the analyst and may last for several years.

psychosomatic   physical symptom in which the mind plays an important part in causing the condition – e.g. blushing and many sexual problems.

psychotherapy   sometimes known as 'talk therapy'; problems are treated by helping people to help themselves. This is achieved by enabling them to change self-defeating patterns of thinking, feeling and behaving.

refractory period   variable period of time during which a nerve is unable to transmit an impulse. In a sexual context, a refractory period is that interval of time in a man when, after an orgasm, he is unable to achieve another climax.

REM sleep   'rapid-eye movement' sleep, so described because, during these periods, amounting perhaps to a quarter of all sleep, people are in a shallow dream sleep during which their eyes move continuously.

retrograde ejaculation   passage of semen at orgasm backwards into the bladder instead of to the exterior through the penis.

sadomasochists   individuals who fail to become aroused sexually unless they either inflict pain (*sadism*) or receive it (*masochism*).

scrotum   sac beneath the penis containing the two testes.

seminal vesicles   paired structures found near the prostate gland and in which much of the semen is made.

sensate focus   that part of a sex therapy programme in which the couple are instructed to 'pleasure' each other. This is achieved by each caressing and massaging the other *in turn*, while at the same time observing a ban on intercourse.

testes   testicles; paired structures in the scrotum of a man, responsible for producing sperm and the sex hormone *testosterone*.

testosterone   sex hormone secreted by the testes and responsible for normal sexual development and function in the male.

thyroid gland   ductless gland found in the neck either side of the windpipe. It secretes the hormone *thyroxine*, which controls the rate at which many body processes take place.

trans-sexual   man or woman who wants to change his or her sex.

transvestite   men (and occasionally women) who cross-dress – that is, those who enjoy wearing the clothes of the opposite sex.

traumatic learning   painful and distressing event(s) which has (have) a prolonged effect upon the subsequent behaviour of a person.

uterus   womb; organ situated at the top of the vagina in which the foetus will develop during pregnancy.

vacuum condoms   appliances capable of creating a partial vacuum and used on the penis to produce an erection.

vagina   tube-like structure between the lips of the vulva and the uterus, into which the penis is inserted during intercourse.

vaginismus   involuntary constriction of the muscles of the lower third of the vagina; this often prevents intercourse or makes the experience extremely painful.

vaginitis   inflammation of the walls of the vagina often caused by infection, but may also be psychosomatic.

Valium (generic name = diazepam)   mild tranquillizer belonging to the group of drugs known as the benzodiazepines.

vasectomy   male sterilization achieved by cutting the tubes that deliver the sperm from the testes. Vasectomy does not affect the amount of semen produced, nor sexual performance.

venous leak   fault in the blood supply to the penis where a failure to get an erection is caused by blood leaking from the arterial supply into the veins, before it has had time to fill the erectile tissue.

vibrator   electrically operated device (either battery or mains) used to help a man or woman obtain an orgasm.

voyeur   usually men who enjoy observing women (and men) in various states of undress or having sex.

vulva   external sex organs of the female. It comprises the labia (lips), the clitoris and the introitus (entrance to the vagina).

NOTES

[1] A.C. Kinsey, W.B. Pomeroy & C. Martin (1948) *Sexual Behavior in the Human Male*, W.B. Saunders, Philadelphia & London.
[2] Deidre Sanders (1987) *The* Woman *Report on Men*, Sphere Books, London.
[3] Martin Cole (1988) 'Normal and dysfunctional sexual behaviour: frequencies and incidences', in Martin Cole & Windy Dryden (eds) *Sex Therapy in Britain*, Open University, Milton Keynes.
[4] W.H. Masters & V.E. Johnson (1970) *Human Sexual Inadequacy*, J. & A. Churchill, London.
[5] Ibid.
[6] Martin Cole (1985) 'Sex therapy – a critical appraisal', *British Journal of Psychiatry*, Vol. 147, pp. 337–51.
[7] Martin Cole (1988) 'Sex therapy for individuals', in Martin Cole & Windy Dryden (eds) *Sex Therapy in Britain*, Open University Press, Milton Keynes.
[8] Kinsey, Pomeroy & Martin, op. cit.
[9] M. Hunt (1974) *Sexual Behavior in the 1970s*, Playboy Press, Chicago.
[10] Cole, 'Normal and dysfunctional sexual behaviour: frequencies and incidences', op. cit.
[11] Martin Cole (1986) 'Socio-sexual characteristics of men with sexual problems', *Sexual and Marital Therapy*, Vol. 1, pp. 89–108.
[12] Ibid.
[13] E. Frank, C. Anderson & D. Rubinstein (1978) 'Frequency of sexual dysfunction in "normal" couples', *New England Journal of Medicine*, Vol. 299, pp. 111–15. P. Nettelbladt & N. Uddenberg (1979) 'Sexual dysfunction and sexual satisfaction in 58 married Swedish men', *Journal of Psychosomatic Research*, Vol. 23, pp. 141–7.
[14] Masters & Johnson, op. cit.
[15] A.C. Kinsey, W.B. Pomeroy, C.E. Martin & P.H. Gebhard (1953) *Sexual Behavior in the Human Female*, W.B. Saunders, Philadelphia & London.
[16] W.H. Masters & V.E. Johnson (1966) *Human Sexual Response*, Little Brown, Boston.
[17] John Bancroft (1983) *Human Sexuality and Its Problems*, Churchill Livingstone, Edinburgh.
[18] Nancy Friday (1988) *My Secret Garden*, Quartet, London.
[19] L.M. Terman (1951) 'Correlates of orgasm adequacy in a group of 556 wives', *Journal of Psychology*, Vol. 32, pp. 115–72. S. Fisher (1973) *The Female Orgasm*, Basic Books, New York.
[20] Bancroft, op. cit.
[21] A.K. Ladas, B. Whipple & J.D. Perry (1982) *The G-spot and Other Recent Discoveries about Human Sexuality*, Holt Rinehart & Winston, New York.

[22] Deidre Sanders (1985) *The* Woman *Book of Love and Sex*, Sphere Books, London.

[23] Cole, 'Normal and dysfunctional sexual behaviours: frequencies and incidences', op. cit.

[24] Masters & Johnson, *Human Sexual Inadequacy*, op. cit.

[25] Cole, 'Normal and dysfunctional sexual behaviours: frequencies and incidences', op. cit.

[26] Kinsey, Pomeroy & Martin, op. cit.

[27] Kinsey, Pomeroy, Martin & Gebhard, op. cit.

[28] Paul H. Gebhard & Alan Johnson (1979) *The Kinsey Data*, W.B. Saunders, Philadelphia & London.

[29] F. Kallmann (1952) 'Comparative twin study on the genetic aspects of male homosexuality', *Journal of Nervous and Mental Disorders*, Vol. 115, pp. 283–98.

[30] I. Bieber *et al* (1962) *Homosexuality: a psychoanalytic study*, Basic Books, New York. E. Bene (1965) 'On the genesis of male homosexuality: an attempt at clarifying the role of the parents', *British Journal of Psychiatry*, Vol. 111, pp. 803–13.

[31] Kallmann, op. cit.

[32] Bieber *et al*, op. cit.

[33] M. Siegelman (1974) 'Parental background of male homosexuals and heterosexuals', *Archives of Sexual Behavior*, Vol. 3, pp. 3–18. A.P. Bell, M.S. Weinberg & S.K. Hammersmith (1981) *Sexual Preference – Its Development in Men and Women*, Indiana University Press, Bloomington.

[34] C. Wolff (1971) *Love Between Women*, Harper & Row, New York.

[35] Christine Dancey (1988) Personal communication to the authors.

[36] W.H. Masters, V.E. Johnson & R.C. Kolodny (1987) *Sex and Human Loving*, Papermac, London.

[37] R.C. Kolodny, W.H. Masters, B.S. Hendryx & G. Toro (1971) 'Plasma testosterone and semen analysis in male homosexuals', *New England Journal of Medicine*, Vol. 285, pp. 1170–4.

[38] G. Dörner, W. Rohde, F. Stahl, L. Krell & W.C. Masius (1975) 'A neuroendocrine predisposition for homosexuality in men', *Archives of Sexual Behavior*, Vol. 4, pp. 1–8.

[39] Berl Kutschinsky (1970) *Studies in Pornography and Sex Crimes in Denmark*, New Social Science Monographs, Copenhagen.

[40] Kinsey, Pomeroy & Martin, op. cit.

[41] G.D. Wilson & D.N. Cox (1983) *The Child-Lovers: a study of paedophiles in society*, Peter Owen, London.

[42] G.D. Wilson (1988) 'The sociobiological basis of sexual dysfunction', in Martin Cole & Windy Dryden (eds) *Sex Therapy in Britain*, Open University Press, Milton Keynes.

[43] Bancroft, op. cit.

[44] David H. Barlow (1986) 'Causes of sexual dysfunctions: the role of anxiety and cognitive interference', *Journal of Consulting and Clinical Psychology*, Vol. 54 (2), pp. 140–8.

[45] Minerva (1988) 'News and Notes', *British Medical Journal*, Vol. 296, p. 866.

INDEX

Page numbers in *italic* refer to the illustrations